Foundation Science
P H Y S I C S

FOR CLASS 10

H C Verma, PhD

Bharati Bhawan
PUBLISHERS & DISTRIBUTORS

Published by

BHARATI BHAWAN (Publishers & Distributors)

4271/3 Ansari Road, Daryaganj, NEW DELHI 110 002, Phone: 23286557
A-61 B/2 Sector 63, NOIDA 201 307, Phone: 4757400
Thakurbari Road, PATNA 800 003, Phone: 2670325
10 Raja Subodh Mallick Square, KOLKATA 700 013, Phone: 22250651
No. 98 Sirsi Circle, Mysore Road, BENGALURU 560 018, Phone: 26740560
Hemsee Heights, Kutchery, Circular Road, RANCHI 834 001, Phone: 2361066

First edition 2003
Fourth edition 2011
Reset print 2013
2016 print

Every genuine copy of the book has a hologram sticker that is different from ordinary stickers.

1. By moving the book you can see motion in the elements in the upper part of the hologram.

2. There are microscopic letters in the balls in the upper part of the hologram.

3. The lower part has round mirrors in which you can see your reflection.

4. Each hologram has its own number.

Foundation Science: Physics for Class 10
Printed at B B Printers, Patna-800 006

PREFACE

It gives me great pleasure in presenting the third edition of this book. The contents of the book have changed quite a bit to reflect the new syllabus of the Central Board of Secondary Education. Not only have new topics been added, older ones have been thoroughly revised.

The basic philosophy and writing style of the book remain the same. The goal is to provide students with a strong foundation in science. Common, everyday experiences are widely used to illustrate scientific principles. This should make the reading interesting as well as help students realize the intimate relationship between science and nature. When a new equation is derived or a new concept is introduced, generally, a numerical example follows. These in-text numerical examples should help in clarifying the exact meaning of the terms in the equation and in the elaboration of the concept. The main points discussed in a chapter are collected at one place under the heading *Points to Remember.* This should help students in quickly revising the chapter, but I strongly discourage depending too heavily on this section. In each chapter a separate section on solved problems illustrates how the equations and laws discussed in that chapter can be used in working out problems.

The exercises in each chapter has several types of questions such as multiple-choice questions, filling in the blanks, marking statements true or false, numerical problems, etc. In examinations, students need to answer some questions within a certain number of words. In the exercises you will find questions categorized on the basis of the word limits of their answers. *Very-short-answer questions* have to be answered in one word or maximum in one sentence. Depending on the question, *short-answer questions* have to be answered in 30–40 words or 40–50 words. And the length of the answers of *long-answer questions* can vary from 70 to 100 words. The exact word limit is mentioned in the question paper. These exhaustive exercises, I hope, will prepare the students for their Board examinations, as well as, for higher studies.

The exercises are not only to test the understanding of the students, but also to make it better. A carefully formulated exercise problem encourages the student to think deeply about the principles involved and in the process makes his understanding of the concept clearer. I have tried my best to formulate exercise sets to stimulate the minds of the students.

A special section called *Postscript* is given at the end of some chapters. In this section, I have given some interesting facts related to the subject of that chapter. In some cases simple activities or projects are suggested. These activities can be performed without any special equipment. I hope students will enjoy this section.

Author

CONTENTS

❏

First term: Chapters 4, 5 and 6
Second term: Chapters 1, 2 and 3

CONTENTS

Reflection of Light

'Seeing' is one of the most common things we do. When light from an object enters our eyes, we see the object. This light can be that emitted by the object, as in the case of an electric bulb or a red-hot iron nail. It can also be the light bouncing off an object like a book. An object that emits light is a source of light. During the day, the sun acts as a natural source of light. Candles, oil lamps and electric bulbs are sources of light made by us.

What is the nature of light? Is it made of material particles like electrons, protons or neutrons, or is it something else? Does a source of light emit 'particles' of light, or does it cause some kind of wave motion in the space around it? For centuries, scientists struggled with this question. Although most common phenomena involving light can be understood by thinking of light as a wave, certain phenomena can be explained only if we think of light as being made up of particles. Scientists now understand that light shows the characteristics of both a wave and a particle.

Some Properties of Light

- Light does not need a material medium to travel, i.e., it can travel through a vacuum too. The best example of this is light travelling from the sun to the earth across vast expanses of space that have no material (or matter). Compare this with sound, which is also a wave. Sound needs a material medium to travel.

- Light waves travel at a tremendous speed—whose value scientists have fixed at 299,792,458 m/s. According to current scientific theories, no material particle can travel at a speed greater than that of light.

- The light that enables us to see has a very small wavelength—less than ten thousandth part of a centimetre. In comparison, the wavelength of audible sound is of the order of a few centimetres to a few metres.

Propagation of Light

Light travels along straight lines in a medium or in vacuum. The path of light changes only when there is an object in its path or where the medium changes. We call this rectilinear (straight-line) propagation of light. Light that starts from a point A and passes through another point B in the same medium actually passes through all the points on the straight line AB. Such a straight-line path of light is called a ray of light. Light rays start from each point of a source and travel along straight lines till they fall on an object or a surface separating two media (mediums). A bundle of light rays is called a beam of light.

Apart from vacuum and gases, light can travel through some liquids and solids. A medium in which light can travel freely over large distances is called a transparent medium. Water, glycerine, glass and clear plastics are transparent. A medium in which light cannot travel is called opaque. Wood, metals, bricks, etc., are opaque. In materials like oil, light can travel some distance, but its intensity reduces rapidly. Such materials are called translucent.

REFLECTION OF LIGHT

When light falls on a smooth surface, a part of it gets reflected. Figure 1.1 shows a ray of light being reflected from a flat, smooth surface. The ray *AO* is incident on the surface at point *O* and is reflected along *OB*. The line *ON* is the normal to the surface at *O*. This means, *ON* is perpendicular to the surface. The angle *AON* that the incident ray makes with the normal is called the angle of incidence, commonly denoted by *i*. And the angle *BON* that the reflected ray makes with the normal is called the angle of reflection, commonly denoted by *r*.

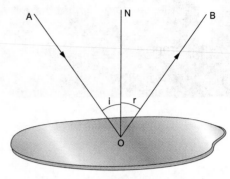

Fig. 1.1

The reflection of light follows two laws.

➤ **Laws of Reflection**	1. *The angle of incidence and the angle of reflection are equal.* 2. *The incident ray, the reflected ray and the normal to the surface at the point of incidence are in the same plane.*

In Figure 1.1, ∠*AON* = ∠*BON*, and the three lines *AO*, *OB* and *ON* are in the same plane.

The same laws hold for reflection from a curved surface as well. We can determine the path of the reflected ray by drawing the normal to the curved surface at the point of incidence of light. To draw a normal at a point (*O*) on a curved surface, first draw a tangent (*PQ*) to the surface at that point (Figure 1.2). A normal (*ON*) to this tangent is also normal to the curved surface. For a spherical surface, a radius through a point on the surface is normal to the surface.

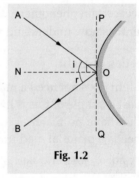

Fig. 1.2

Images Formed by Reflection

When light starting from an object is reflected off a smooth surface and reaches our eyes, we see an image of the object. The images formed by mirrors are the most common examples of images formed by reflection. Images are also formed when light reflects off shiny metal surfaces, the calm surface of the water in a pond, and so on.

Reflection from plane mirrors

Plane mirrors are commonly used as looking glasses. We use them while dressing, combing, and so on. A plane mirror is made from a glass plate, a few millimetres thick. One surface of the glass is polished to a high degree of smoothness, forming the front surface of the mirror. The back surface is *silvered*, i.e., coated with a thin layer of silver, aluminium or some other shiny, opaque material. A coat of opaque paint behind this layer protects the silvering. When light from an object falls on the front surface, most of it enters the glass plate and falls on the silvered surface.

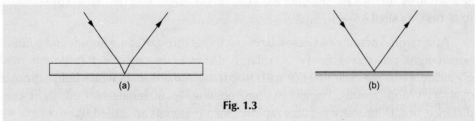

(a)   (b)

Fig. 1.3

It gets reflected from there and goes out from the front surface (Figure 1.3a). Generally, we neglect the thickness of the glass plate and think of the mirror as a single surface. Hatching (or other shading) behind the surface represents silvering (Figure 1.3b).

Properties of image formed by plane mirrors In previous classes you have learnt about the properties of an image formed by a plane mirror. The list below will help you recall them.

- A plane mirror forms a virtual image. Such an image is not formed by the actual intersection of light rays and cannot be formed on a screen.
- The image formed by a plane mirror is erect. So, the image of a person formed by a plane mirror has the head at the top and the feet at the bottom.
- The image is formed as far behind the mirror as the object is in front of it.
- The size of the image formed by a plane mirror is equal to that of the object.
- The image is laterally inverted. This means that in the image formed by a plane mirror, the left and right sides are reversed.

Fig. 1.4 Lateral inversion by a plane mirror

Reflection from curved surfaces

Images can be formed by the reflection of light from smooth, curved surfaces like doorknobs, taps, utensils, etc. Hold a large, shiny spoon in front of your face. In spoons, one curved surface is hollow while the other bulges out. Depending on which surface of the spoon you are looking at, you will see different kinds of images of your face. Let us find out a bit more about the images formed by the curved surfaces of spoons.

Place a lighted candle in front of a large, shiny spoon. For each side of the spoon, check the following.

- Is the image formed erect or inverted?
- What is the size of the image compared to that of the candle (larger/smaller/same-sized)?
- Change the distance between the spoon and the candle. Does the size of the image change?
- As you bring the spoon close to the candle, does the image of the candle disappear at a certain distance?

Fig. 1.5

The images formed by the two surfaces of the spoon are similar to those formed by curved mirrors. We shall now learn about some types of curved mirrors.

Spherical Mirrors

Spherical mirrors are special types of curved mirrors in which the surface of the mirror is a part of a sphere. The rear-view mirrors in cars, scooters, etc., are spherical mirrors. They can be thought of as being made from a portion cut off from a hollow glass sphere (Figure 1.6). Such a portion has

Fig. 1.6 A spherical mirror can be thought of as being made of a portion cut off from a hollow glass sphere.

two dissimilar surfaces. The hollow surface that is on the same side as the centre of the original sphere is called the concave surface. The other surface, which bulges out, is called the convex surface. If the convex surface is polished and the concave surface is silvered, we get a convex mirror. And if the concave surface is polished and the convex surface is silvered, we get a concave mirror.

Light falling on the smooth surface of a spherical mirror enters the glass and is reflected at the opaque silvered surface. Again, we neglect the thickness of the glass and represent the spherical mirror by a single curved surface.

Spherical Mirror Terms

Pole The central point on the surface of the mirror is called its pole.

Centre of curvature and radius of curvature The centre of the sphere of which the spherical mirror is a part is called the centre of curvature of the mirror. The radius of this sphere is called the radius of curvature of the mirror.

It is clear from the parts a and b of Figure 1.7 that the centre of curvature lies in front of the mirror in the case of a concave mirror and it lies behind the mirror in the case of a convex mirror.

A line joining the centre of curvature to a point on the mirror is, from geometry, normal to the curved surface at that point.

Principal axis The line joining the pole and the centre of curvature is called the principal axis of the mirror.

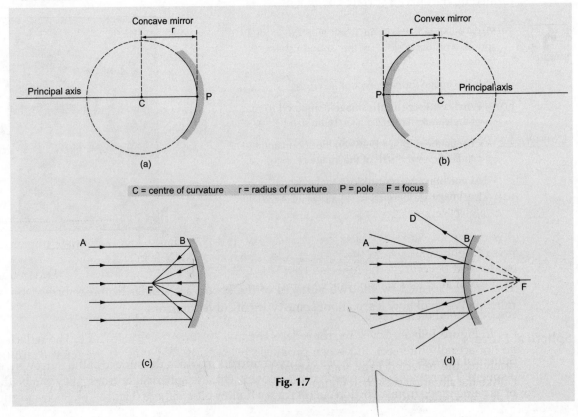

Fig. 1.7

Aperture The circular area that determines the amount of light falling on a mirror or a lens is its aperture. In case of a spherical mirror, the area of the circle made by its boundary is its aperture. Sometimes, the aperture of a spherical mirror is expressed in terms of the diameter of its boundary. Thus, a mirror of 2-cm aperture would mean that the diameter of its boundary is 2 cm.

Focus and focal length In Figure 1.7c, a ray AB, parallel to the principal axis, is incident on a concave mirror. After reflection, the ray cuts the principal axis at a point F. In fact, if the aperture of the mirror is small, all rays incident parallel to the principal axis will cut the principal axis at this same point F after reflection. In other words, such incident rays *converge* to F. A concave mirror is therefore also called a converging mirror.

In Figure 1.7d, a ray AB, parallel to the principal axis, is incident on a convex mirror. The ray is reflected along BD. When BD is produced backwards, it intersects the principal axis at F. For a convex mirror of small aperture, all rays incident parallel to the principal axis, when produced backwards after reflection, appear to *diverge* from this same point F. A convex mirror is therefore also called a diverging mirror. We can now define focus and focal length of a spherical mirror as follows.

> The point on the principal axis where rays incident parallel to the principal axis converge to or appear to diverge from after reflection is called the focus of the spherical mirror. The distance of the focus from the pole is called the focal length of the spherical mirror.

An incident ray passing (or appearing to pass) through the focus becomes parallel to the principal axis after reflection. You can see this by reversing the direction of the arrows in Figure 1.7.

Let us find the focal length of a concave mirror. Face the concave mirror towards the sun. Take a small piece of paper and fix it to a thin stick. Using the stick as a handle, hold the paper very close to the mirror. Now gradually take the paper away from the mirror, towards the sun. At all times hold the paper at a small angle to the mirror to allow sunlight to fall on the mirror.

After a certain distance you will see an oval spot on the paper. Adjust the position and the angle of the paper till you get a very small, almost round, bright spot. At this position measure the distance between the pole of the mirror and the paper. This distance is the approximate focal length of the mirror. If you keep the paper there for some time, the paper will start burning because sunlight gets concentrated at one spot, producing a lot of heat.

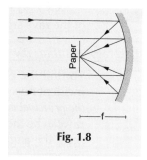

Fig. 1.8

Relation between focal length and radius of curvature The focal length f and the radius of curvature r of a spherical mirror of small aperture are related as

$$f = \frac{r}{2}$$

...1.1

From this it is clear that the centre of curvature is at a distance of $r = 2f$ from the pole of the mirror.

EXAMPLE 1.1 A concave mirror is made by cutting a portion of a hollow glass sphere of radius 24 cm. Find the focal length of the mirror.

Solution The radius of curvature of the mirror = 24 cm.
Thus, the focal length = 24 cm/2 = 12 cm.

....

Real and virtual images Consider the situation shown in Figure 1.9a. A concave mirror reflects rays of light coming from the point A. The reflected rays intersect at the point A'. To a person's eye located beyond A', the reflected rays will appear to come from A'. Hence, the eye will see an image of A at A'. If a screen is placed at A', the rays will intersect on the screen, forming an image on it. An image formed by the actual intersection of light rays is called a real image. A real image can be formed on a screen.

In Figure 1.9b, a convex mirror reflects the rays starting from the point B. The reflected rays do not actually intersect. But when produced backwards, they meet at the point B'. To the eye receiving the reflected rays, they appear to come from B', and hence, an image is seen there. Unlike the situation shown in Figure 1.9a, no light reaches B', where the image is formed. Such an image, as you know, is called a virtual image. If the rays of light responsible for an image do not

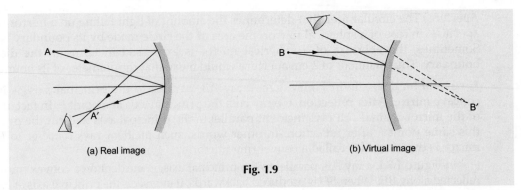

(a) Real image   (b) Virtual image

Fig. 1.9

actually intersect, the image is called a virtual image. A virtual image cannot be formed on a screen, as no light reaches where the image appears to be.

Note that in both cases the image is formed at the point of intersection of the lines representing the reflected rays.

Finding the Image by Ray Tracing

Numerous rays of light starting from a point object placed before a spherical mirror fall on the mirror and get reflected. The image of the object is formed at the point of intersection of the reflected rays. Ray tracing means locating the image geometrically. This is done by drawing some of the rays and finding the point of intersection of the reflected rays.

Two rays useful for ray tracing

To find the point of intersection of the reflected rays, you need any two rays. We choose two incident rays that get reflected along known paths. The first can be *the ray that is incident parallel to the principal axis*. After reflection, it passes through the focus, which is a known point. The other ray can be the one *that is incident perpendicular to the mirror's surface*. Since its angle of incidence is zero, the angle of reflection is also zero, i.e., the ray turns right back, or *retraces its path*. Being perpendicular to the spherical surface, the ray (or its projection backwards) passes through the centre of curvature, another known point.

Finding the image of point objects

For a convex mirror Figure 1.10 illustrates this method for a convex mirror. Starting from the point object *A*, draw the ray *AD*, parallel to the principal axis. The reflected ray when produced backwards should pass through the focus, *F*. So, join *FD* using dashed lines, and extend it to *G* to get the reflected ray *DG*. Now draw a line joining *A* to the centre of curvature *C*, as shown. This line is normal to the mirror and cuts it at *E*. So, the incident ray *AE* retraces its path along *EA*. The backward projections of the two reflected rays intersect at *A'*, which is the virtual image of *A*.

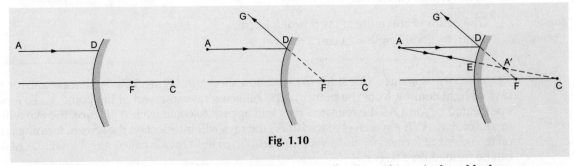

Fig. 1.10

For a concave mirror We shall now locate the image of a point object *A* placed before a concave mirror (Figure 1.11). First draw a ray *AD* parallel to the principal axis. After reflection, this ray will pass through the focus, *F*. Then draw a ray *AE* through the centre of curvature, *C*. Since it is incident normal to the mirror at *E*, it will retrace its path along *EC*. The reflected rays actually intersect at *A'*, where the real image of *A* is formed.

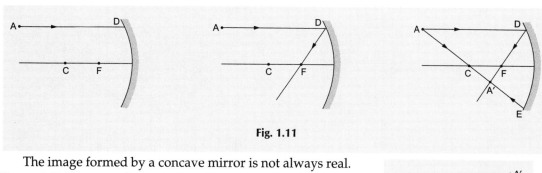

Fig. 1.11

The image formed by a concave mirror is not always real. Figure 1.12 shows such a case. As usual, we have chosen two rays—*AD*, parallel to the principal axis, and *AE*, passing through the centre of curvature. After reflection, *AD* passes through *F*, and *AE* retraces its path. You will notice that the reflected rays diverge. So they can never actually intersect. However, if they are produced backwards, they meet at *A'*, where the virtual image of *A* is formed.

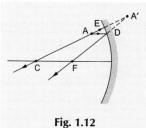

Fig. 1.12

When the point object is on the principal axis Let us consider a point object *O* placed on the principal axis of a spherical mirror (Figure 1.13 shows this for both types of spherical mirrors). A ray *OP* along the principal axis falls normally on the mirror and, therefore, retraces its path. Take any other ray *OA*, incident on the mirror at *A*. Let the reflected ray (or its projection backwards) cut the principal axis at *I*. As *I* is the point of intersection of the reflected rays, it is the image of *O*. All reflected rays will pass through (or seem to pass through) it. Thus, *the image of a point on the principal axis is formed on the principal axis itself.*

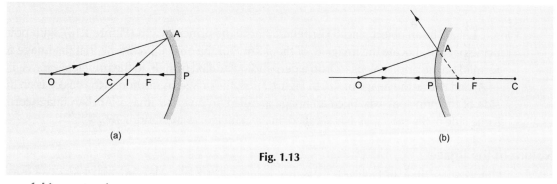

(a)   (b)

Fig. 1.13

Other rays useful in ray tracing

The two special incident rays mentioned above are generally sufficient to locate an image formed by a spherical mirror. In addition, you can consider a ray that falls obliquely on the mirror after passing through the focus. After reflection, this ray becomes parallel to the principal axis, as shown in Figure 1.14.

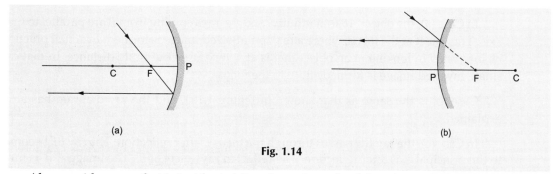

(a)   (b)

Fig. 1.14

Also consider a ray that is incident obliquely on the pole of the mirror. At the pole, the normal to the mirror is its principal axis. So, the principal axis will make equal angles with the incident and reflected rays (law of reflection). Using this, the reflected ray can be drawn.

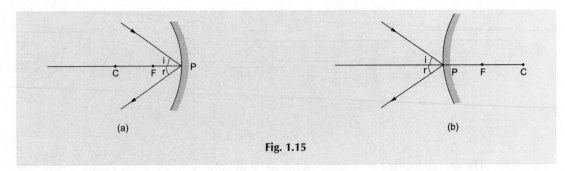

(a)

(b)

Fig. 1.15

Finding the image of extended objects

The image of an extended object formed by a spherical mirror can be found by locating the images of the individual points of the object. One case of interest is that of a small, linear object placed on the principal axis, perpendicular to it. We can find the whole image by just locating the images of the points at the top and bottom of the object.

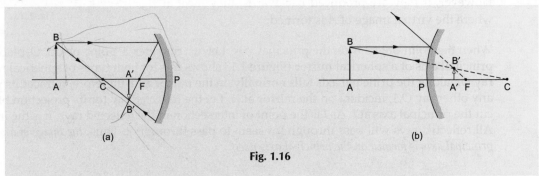

(a)

(b)

Fig. 1.16

Let AB be an object placed perpendicular to the principal axis (Figure 1.16), with point A on the principal axis. Locate the image B' of the point B of the object. We know that the image of A will be formed on the principal axis. Drop a perpendicular $B'A'$ from B' to the principal axis. A' is the image of A, and $A'B'$ is the image of AB. In Figure 1.16a, the image, in relation to the object, is on the opposite side of the principal axis. Such an image is called an inverted image. And an image formed on the same side of the principal axis is called an erect image, as in Figure 1.16b.

Nature of the Image

The size, location and nature of the image formed by a spherical mirror depend on the position of the object.

Images formed by a concave mirror

Table 1.1 shows the formation of image by a concave mirror in several situations. You should carefully study each ray diagram and verify its entries in the table.

In Case (a), the object AB is at infinity, and the rays coming from B are parallel to the principal axis. They meet at the focus, where a real, point-sized image is formed. In actual practice, we may be interested in looking at an object that is at a very large but finite distance. In that case, a very small, inverted image is formed, close to the focus.

Case (b) is the same as that shown in Figure 1.16a, and the ray diagram has already been explained.

In Case (c), the ray BD passes through the focus F after reflection. The ray BF becomes parallel to the principal axis after reflection. The reflected rays meet at B'. The image $A'B'$ is inverted, has the same size as the object and is formed at the same distance from the mirror.

In Case (d), the reflected rays intersect beyond C and an enlarged (magnified), inverted image is formed.

Table 1.1 Images formed by concave mirrors

	Object position	Image position	Nature of image
(a)	at infinity	at the focus F	real and point-sized
(b)	between infinity and the centre of curvature C	between F and C	real, smaller than the object, inverted
(c)	at C	at C	real, same size, inverted
(d)	between C and F	between C and infinity	real, enlarged, inverted
(e)	at F *	at infinity	real, infinitely large, inverted
(f)	between the pole P and F	behind the mirror	virtual, enlarged, erect

* One can also say that the image is formed behind the mirror and is virtual and erect in this case. In fact, this is more practical from the observer's point of view.

Case (e) needs special attention. The object *AB* is placed at the focus. The point *A* is on the focus. The ray *BD* is parallel to the principal axis. It passes through the point *A* after reflection. The ray *BE* passes through *C* and retraces its path. The reflected rays *DA* and *EB* turn out to be parallel. We can say that they intersect at infinity to form a real image of *B* below the principal axis. In this sense, the image of *AB* can be considered real and inverted. However, when the reflected rays fall on the eye, they appear to come from a point behind the mirror, above the principal axis. In this sense, the image may be considered virtual and erect.

In Case (f), rays coming from *B* diverge after reflection. If the reflected rays are produced backwards, they meet at *B'*. To the eye, the reflected rays appear to come from *B'*. Thus *B'* is the image of *B*, and *A'B'* is the image of *AB*. It is a virtual image because the rays do not actually intersect. The size of the image is larger than that of the object, and the image is erect.

EXAMPLE 1.2   **We want a concave mirror to form a virtual image of an object. See Table 1.1 and find out where the object should be placed. Is the image erect or inverted? Is the image smaller or larger than the object?**

Solution   We see from Table 1.1 that a concave mirror forms a virtual image of an object when the object is placed between the pole and the focus. The image is erect and larger than the object.

Images formed by a convex mirror

In a convex mirror, the image is always formed behind the mirror, between the pole and the focus. The image is always virtual, erect and smaller than the object. As the object moves away from the mirror, its image moves towards the focus. And when the object is at infinity, the image is formed at the focus. Image formation by a convex mirror is shown in Table 1.2.

If you place a small plane mirror in front of a large building, you will be able to see only a part of the building in the mirror. However, if you place a convex mirror of small focal length at the same place, you may be able to see the whole building. That is because convex mirrors form images that are smaller than the objects. So we are able to see the images of wide areas in them.

After going through the tables on the formation of images by spherical mirrors, you would have noticed that the real images formed by spherical mirrors are always inverted and the virtual images are always erect.

Table 1.2 Images formed by convex mirrors

		Object position	Image position	Nature of image
(a)		between infinity and the pole	between the focus and the pole	virtual, smaller and erect
(b)		at infinity	at the focus *F*	virtual, point-sized

Let us study the nature of the images formed by a concave mirror. First find the approximate focal length (f) of a concave mirror, as explained before. Then fix it vertically on a stand. Draw a long straight line on a table and place the mirror stand on it. The pole of the mirror should be exactly above the line. Now mark the points F and C on the line, at distances f and $2f$ respectively from the mirror.

Make a small screen of stiff paper and fix it on another stand. The screen should be vertical, with its centre at about the same height as the pole of the mirror. Place the screen stand on the line drawn on the table.

Light a candle and place it between F and C. The flame of the candle should be at about the same height as the pole of the mirror. Move the screen back and forth till you see an inverted, enlarged and sharp image of the flame on the screen. Does the image match the description given at (d) in Table 1.1? Keep the candle at different positions and try to get its image on the screen. See if you can verify the other entries of Table 1.1.

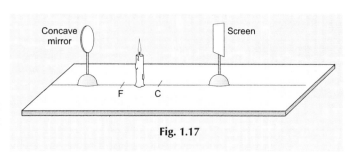

Fig. 1.17

Sign Convention

With spherical mirrors, we generally come across four distances parallel to and two distances perpendicular to the principal axis. Each of these six distances has a particular mathematical quantity associated with it. These quantities are given in Table 1.3.

Table 1.3

Distance	Quantity	Symbol
From the pole to the object	object-distance	u
From the pole to the image	image-distance	v
From the pole to the focus	focal length	f
From the pole to the centre	radius of curvature	r
Height of the object	object-height	h_o
Height of the image	image-height	h_e

The above definitions of u and v are for a point object placed on the principal axis. If an object is placed away from the principal axis, u corresponds to the distance from the pole to the foot of the perpendicular drawn from the object to the principal axis. Similarly, v corresponds to the distance from the pole to the foot of the perpendicular drawn from the image to the principal axis. The quantities h_o and h_e are defined for a linear, extended object placed perpendicular to the principal axis.

For finding a particular distance when some others are given, we need to assign these quantities (u, v, f, r, h_o, h_e) positive or negative signs according to a fixed set of rules, or a convention. Several conventions for the signs of these quantities are in use. We shall follow the Cartesian coordinates convention.

The sign convention for the distances parallel to the principal axis is as follows.

Coordinate Convention for u, v, f, r	• *u, v, f and r are measured from the pole.* • *If a distance is measured along the incident rays, the corresponding quantity is positive. If a distance is measured opposite to the incident rays, the corresponding quantity is negative.*

For example, in Figure 1.16a, the rays are incident from the left to the right. To measure the object-distance we have to measure from the pole to the object, i.e., from the right to the left. This direction is opposite to that of the incident rays. The object-distance u is, therefore, negative. In other words, $u = -PA$. The image $A'B'$, the focus F and the centre of curvature C are also to the left of the pole P. Thus, v, f and r are also negative in the given case.

In Figure 1.16b, the image is on the right of the pole. The image-distance is measured from the pole to the image, i.e., along the incident rays. The image-distance v is, therefore, positive. As you can see from the figure, u is negative, whereas, v, f and r are positive. Note that the object-distance u is always negative for a real object.

Let us now state the sign convention for distances perpendicular to the principal axis.

> | **Coordinate Convention for h_o, h_e** | • *The object-height h_o is always taken as positive. If the image is formed on the same side of the principal axis (erect image), the image-height h_e is also positive. If the image is formed on the opposite side (inverted image), h_e is negative.* |
> |---|---|

In Figure 1.16a, h_o is positive but h_e is negative. In Figure 1.16b, both h_o and h_e are positive.

Why is this sign convention called the 'coordinate convention'? It is called so because if, by convention, we always keep the object to the left of the pole and above the principal axis, the signs of the quantities u, v, f and r follow the same rules followed for representing the x-coordinates of points using coordinate axes. You can think of the pole as the origin, the principal axis as the x-axis and a line perpendicular to it as the y-axis. The left-to-right direction is taken as the positive direction of the x-axis. Then you can think of u, v, f and r as the x-coordinates of the object, image, focus and centre of curvature respectively. Thus, if any of these is to the left of the pole (origin), its x-coordinate is negative. Similarly, if any of these is to the right of the pole, its x-coordinate is positive. *Since the object, by convention, is always placed to the left of the mirror, its x-coordinate u is always negative.* In both cases shown in Figure 1.16, $u = -PA$. In Figure 1.16a, the image A', the focus F and the centre of curvature C are all to the left of the origin P. So, v, f and r are also negative, and are equal to $-PA', -PF$ and $-PC$ respectively. In Figure 1.16b, the image is to the right of the origin. Hence, its x-coordinate v is positive. Similarly, f and r are also positive.

Note that in this convention, f and r are negative for a concave mirror and positive for a convex mirror. Also, heights above the principal axis are positive and those below it are negative.

The sign convention is summarized in Figure 1.18.

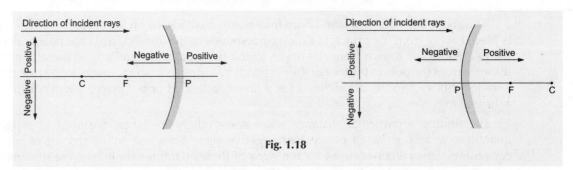

Fig. 1.18

The Mirror Equation: Relation between u, v, f

For any spherical mirror of small aperture, and for any position of the object, the three quantities u, v and f satisfy the simple algebraic relation given below.

Mirror Equation	$\dfrac{1}{v} + \dfrac{1}{u} = \dfrac{1}{f}$	...**1.2**

Remember that u, v, f can be positive or negative depending on the geometry of the situation.

EXAMPLE 1.3 An object is placed at a distance of 30 cm from a concave mirror of focal length 20 cm. Where will the image be formed?

Solution

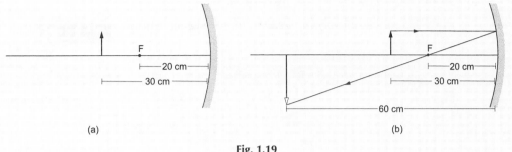

(a)   (b)

Fig. 1.19

The given situation is shown in Figure 1.19a.

We have, $u = -30$ cm and $f = -20$ cm.

Also,
$$\frac{1}{v} + \frac{1}{u} = \frac{1}{f}$$

or
$$\frac{1}{v} = \frac{1}{f} - \frac{1}{u}$$

$$= \frac{1}{-20 \text{ cm}} - \frac{1}{-30 \text{ cm}} = -\frac{1}{60 \text{ cm}}$$

or
$$v = -60 \text{ cm}.$$

So, the image will be formed 60 cm from the mirror. Since v has a negative sign, the image is formed to the left of the mirror, i.e., in front of it, as shown in Figure 1.19b.

Magnification

The size of an image formed by a plane mirror is the same as that of the object. This is not always the case with spherical mirrors. A convex mirror forms an image that is smaller than the object. You might have noticed this in the rear-view mirrors of vehicles. The size of the image formed by a concave mirror can be smaller than, equal to or larger than the size of the object, depending on where the object is placed in front of the mirror.

Let h_o and h_e denote the object-height and the image-height respectively. The ratio $\frac{h_e}{h_o}$ is called magnification, and it is denoted by m. It turns out that

$$m = \frac{h_e}{h_o} = -\frac{v}{u}.$$

Thus,
$$m = -\frac{v}{u}$$

...**1.3**

Note that m can be either positive or negative, depending on the nature of the image. If m is positive, h_o and h_e have the same sign. This means that the image is formed on the same side of the principal axis as the object. In other words, the image is erect. If m is negative, the image is inverted.

EXAMPLE 1.4 A 2.0-cm-high object is placed perpendicular to the principal axis of a concave mirror. The distance of the object from the mirror is 30 cm, and its image is formed 60 cm from the mirror, on the same side of the mirror as the object. Find the height of the image formed.

Solution

The situation is shown in Figure 1.20.

We have, $u = -30$ cm and $v = -60$ cm.

Thus, $m = \frac{h_e}{h_o} = -\frac{v}{u} = -\frac{-60 \text{ cm}}{-30 \text{ cm}} = -2$

or $h_e = -2h_o = -2 \times 2.0 \text{ cm} = -4.0 \text{ cm}.$

The height of the image is 4.0 cm. The minus sign shows that it is on the other side of the axis, i.e., it is inverted.

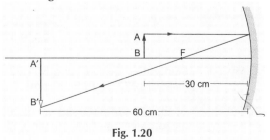

Fig. 1.20

EXAMPLE 1.5 A 1.2-cm-long pin is placed perpendicular to the principal axis of a convex mirror of focal length 12 cm, at a distance of 8 cm from it. **(a)** Find the location of the image. **(b)** Find the height of the image. **(c)** Is the image erect or inverted?

Solution   (a) For a convex mirror, f is positive. So, $f = +12$ cm. Also, $u = -8$ cm.
We have,

$$\frac{1}{v} + \frac{1}{u} = \frac{1}{f}$$

or

$$\frac{1}{v} = \frac{1}{f} - \frac{1}{u} = \frac{1}{12 \text{ cm}} + \frac{1}{8 \text{ cm}} = \frac{5}{24 \text{ cm}}$$

or

$$v = \frac{24}{5} \text{ cm} = 4.8 \text{ cm}.$$

As v is positive, the image is formed on the right of the mirror at a distance of 4.8 cm from it.

(b)

$$m = \frac{h_e}{h_0} = -\frac{v}{u}$$

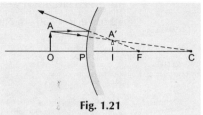

$$= -\frac{4.8 \text{ cm}}{-8 \text{ cm}} = 0.6$$

Fig. 1.21

or

$$h_e = h_0 \times 0.6 = 1.2 \text{ cm} \times 0.6 = 0.72 \text{ cm}.$$

(c) As h_e is positive, the image is on the same side of the principal axis as the object. Thus, the image is erect. Figure 1.21 shows the formation of the image.

Uses of Spherical Mirrors

- Convex mirrors are widely used as rear-view mirrors in cars, scooters, motorcycles, etc. It produces an erect image that is smaller in size than the object. Therefore, a wide view of the traffic behind the vehicle can be seen in a small mirror.

- A concave mirror can produce an erect, enlarged image, behind the mirror. A concave mirror is, therefore, used when you want to see a magnified image of the object. One such use is for shaving, where a magnified view of the face helps to get a smooth shave.

- Dentists use a concave mirror to examine teeth. The large image produced by the mirror help them detect problems.

- Concave mirrors are also used by doctors to focus light on certain parts of the body such as the inside of the ear, inside of the mouth, etc. For this, a bulb is placed at the focus of a concave mirror. Light from the bulb gets reflected to produce a strong, parallel beam. Reflectors used in torches and headlights also work on a similar principle.

- Large concave mirrors can be used to concentrate sunlight to produce heat in some types of solar heating devices. As you might have guessed, in such devices water, food or any other substance that needs to be heated is placed at the focus of a large concave reflector. After reflection, sunlight converges on the substance and heats it.

· SOLVED PROBLEMS ·

EXAMPLE 1 Sunlight is incident on a concave mirror, parallel to its principal axis. The image is formed at a distance of 12 cm from the pole. Find the radius of curvature of the mirror.

Solution   As the rays from the sun are parallel to the principal axis, they form the image at the focus. Thus, the focal length of the mirror is 12 cm. The radius of curvature will be twice the focal length, i.e., 24 cm.

EXAMPLE 2   An object is placed at a distance of 20 cm from a convex mirror of focal length 25 cm. Calculate the position of the image. Discuss its nature.

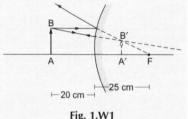

Solution   Here, $u = -20$ cm and $f = +25$ cm.

We have
$$\frac{1}{v} + \frac{1}{u} = \frac{1}{f}$$

or
$$\frac{1}{v} = \frac{1}{f} - \frac{1}{u} = \frac{1}{25 \text{ cm}} - \frac{1}{-20 \text{ cm}} = \frac{9}{100 \text{ cm}}$$

$$v = \frac{100}{9} \text{ cm} \approx 11 \text{ cm}.$$

Fig. 1.W1

The positive sign of v shows that the image is formed on the right, i.e., behind the mirror, as shown in Figure 1.W1. The image is virtual. Also,

$$m = -\frac{v}{u} = -\frac{11}{-20} = +0.55.$$

Since the magnification, and hence, the height of the image is positive, the image is erect.

EXAMPLE 3   A 2.0-cm-high object is placed at a distance of 20 cm from a concave mirror. A real image is formed at 40 cm from the mirror. Calculate the focal length of the mirror and the size of the image.

Solution   The situation is shown in Figure 1.W2. As the image is real, it is formed on the same side as the reflected rays.

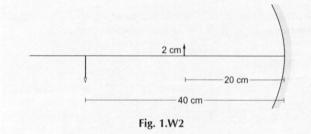

Fig. 1.W2

Here, $u = -20$ cm and $v = -40$ cm.

Thus,
$$\frac{1}{f} = \frac{1}{u} + \frac{1}{v} = \frac{1}{-20 \text{ cm}} + \frac{1}{-40 \text{ cm}} \quad \text{or} \quad f = -13.3 \text{ cm}.$$

The magnification is $m = -\frac{v}{u} = -\frac{-40 \text{ cm}}{-20 \text{ cm}} = -2.$

Thus,
$$\frac{h_e}{h_o} = -2 \quad \text{or} \quad h_e = -2\,h_o = -2 \times 2.0 \text{ cm} = -4.0 \text{ cm}.$$

The height of the image is 4.0 cm, and the negative sign of h_e shows that the image is inverted.

EXAMPLE 4   Find the position, size and the nature of the image formed by a spherical mirror from the following data.
$$u = -20 \text{ cm}, \quad f = -15 \text{ cm}, \quad h_o = 1.0 \text{ cm}$$

Solution   We have
$$\frac{1}{v} + \frac{1}{u} = \frac{1}{f}$$

or
$$\frac{1}{v} = \frac{1}{f} - \frac{1}{u} = \frac{1}{-15 \text{ cm}} - \frac{1}{-20 \text{ cm}} = -\frac{1}{60 \text{ cm}}$$

or $v = -60$ cm.

The image is formed at 60 cm from the mirror. Since the signs of u and v are the same, the image is on the same side as the object (to the left of the mirror), and hence, is real. The magnification is

$$m = \frac{h_e}{h_o} = -\frac{v}{u} = -\frac{-60 \text{ cm}}{-20 \text{ cm}} = -3.$$

So, $h_e = -3h_o = -3 \times 1.0 \text{ cm} = -3.0 \text{ cm}.$

The minus sign shows that the image is inverted. Its size is 3.0 cm.

EXAMPLE 5   A 2-cm-high object is placed at a distance of 32 cm from a concave mirror. The image is real, inverted and 3 cm in size. Find the focal length of the mirror and the position of the image.

Solution   We have, $m = -\dfrac{v}{u} = \dfrac{h_e}{h_o}$.

From the question, $h_e = -3$ cm   and $h_o = 2$ cm.

$\therefore$ $m = \dfrac{h_e}{h_o} = \dfrac{-3 \text{ cm}}{2 \text{ cm}} = -1.5$

or $-\dfrac{v}{u} = -1.5$

or $\dfrac{v}{-32 \text{ cm}} = 1.5$

or $v = -48$ cm.

We have $\dfrac{1}{f} = \dfrac{1}{u} + \dfrac{1}{v} = \dfrac{1}{-32 \text{ cm}} + \dfrac{1}{-48 \text{ cm}} = -\dfrac{5}{96 \text{ cm}}$

or $f = \dfrac{-96 \text{ cm}}{5} = -19.2 \text{ cm}.$

So, the focal length of the concave mirror is 19.2 cm, and the image is formed 48 cm in front of it.

EXAMPLE 6   A concave mirror forms an inverted image of an object placed at a distance of 12 cm from it. If the image is twice as large as the object, where is it formed?

Solution   From the question,

$\dfrac{h_e}{h_o} = -2$ (inverted image)

But $\dfrac{h_e}{h_o} = -\dfrac{v}{u}$

or $\dfrac{v}{u} = 2$

or $v = 2u = 2(-12 \text{ cm}) = -24 \text{ cm}.$

The image is formed at a distance of 24 cm in front of the mirror.

EXAMPLE 7   A concave mirror forms an erect image of an object placed at a distance of 10 cm from it. The size of the image is double that of the object. Where is the image formed?

Solution   From the question,

$\dfrac{h_e}{h_o} = +2$ (erect image)

or $-\dfrac{v}{u} = 2$

or $v = -2u = -2(-10 \text{ cm}) = +20 \text{ cm}.$

Thus, the image is formed 20 cm behind the mirror (from the positive sign of v).

EXAMPLE 8   An object of size 2 cm is placed at a distance of 20 cm from a concave mirror. Its image is inverted, real and 40 cm from the mirror. Draw a scale diagram and locate the focus. Also, measure the focal length and the size of the image.

Solution   We first draw the principal axis PM of the mirror and draw the mirror PD (Figure 1.W3a). Let us choose a scale in which 1 cm (of the drawing) = 5 cm (of the actual situation). In other words, we use a scale of 1 : 5. The object has a size of 2.0 cm. It is shown by the line AB of height 2.0 cm/5 = 0.4 cm. The distance $PA = 20$ cm/5 = 4 cm. The image is formed 40 cm from the pole. We show this point by A'. The length $PA' = 40$ cm/5 = 8 cm. Draw a line $A'N$ perpendicular to the principal axis. The image of B must be on this line.

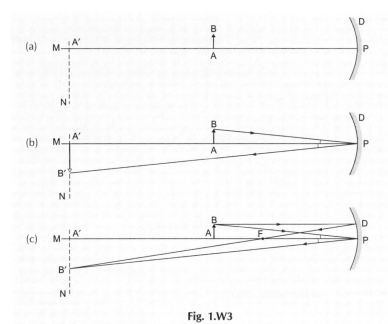

Fig. 1.W3

To get the image of B, we join B to P (Figure 1.W3b). Suppose a ray is incident along BP. The angle of incidence is BPM. Draw the reflected ray PB', making the angle MPB' = the angle BPM. The intersection of this ray with $A'N$ will be the image B' of the point B.

We can now measure the length $A'B'$. It is close to 0.8 cm. So, the size of the image is 0.8 cm × 5 = 4.0 cm. To get the focus, we draw a line BD parallel to the principal axis (Figure 1.W3c). Join D to B'. DB' is the reflected ray corresponding to the incident ray BD. As BD is parallel to the principal axis, the reflected ray cuts the principal axis at the focus. So, we get the focus F. The length PF can now be measured. It is close to 2.7 cm. The focal length of the mirror is, therefore, approximately 2.7 cm × 5 = 13.5 cm.

· POINTS TO REMEMBER ·

• *Laws of reflection*

1. The angle of incidence and the angle of reflection are equal.
2. The incident ray, the reflected ray and the normal to the surface at the point of incidence are in the same plane.

• *Plane mirrors*

The image formed by a plane mirror is virtual, erect, laterally inverted, of the same size as the object, and at the same distance from the mirror as the object.

• *Spherical mirrors*

A spherical mirror is a part of a sphere. The centre of this sphere is called the *centre of curvature* of the mirror. The central point of the surface of the mirror is called its *pole*. The line joining the pole and the centre of curvature is called the *principal axis*. The circular area that determines the amount of light falling on a mirror or a lens is called its *aperture*.

• *Focus and focal length of a spherical mirror*

The point on the principal axis where rays incident parallel to the principal axis converge to or appear to diverge from is called the *focus*.

The distance of the focus from the pole is called the *focal length* of the spherical mirror.

• *Real and virtual images*

If the reflected rays converge at a point, a real image is formed at that point. If they appear to diverge from a point, a virtual image is formed at that point.

• *Image formed by a spherical mirror*

A concave mirror can form a real as well as a virtual image. If the image is real, it is inverted. If the image is virtual, it is erect. The size of the image can be smaller than, equal to or larger than the size of the object.

A convex mirror always forms a virtual, erect and smaller image.

• *Sign convention*

The quantities u, v, f and r denote the positions of the object, the image, the focus and the centre of curvature as measured from the pole. The sign of the quantity is positive if the corresponding distance is measured along the incident rays, and it is negative if the distance is measured opposite to the incident rays.

• *Magnification*

The quantity h_e/h_o is called magnification. Its magnitude indicates how many times is the size of the image as compared to that of the object, and its sign indicates whether it is erect or inverted. Positive sign indicates an erect image and negative sign, an inverted image.

• *Mathematical relations*

For spherical mirrors	$f = \dfrac{r}{2}$
	$\dfrac{1}{v} + \dfrac{1}{u} = \dfrac{1}{f}$
	$m = \dfrac{h_e}{h_o} = -\dfrac{v}{u}$

· EXERCISES ·

A. Very-Short-Answer Questions

1. From which surface of a mirror—the polished surface or the silvered surface—does most of the light reflect?

2. In which kinds of mirrors—plane, concave or convex—can you get a virtual image of an object placed in front of it?

3. What is the principal axis of a spherical mirror?

4. A concave mirror forms a real image of the same size as that of the object. Where is the object placed?

5. Can a convex mirror form a real image of an object?

6. A ray *ACB* is incident on a spherical mirror whose centre of curvature is *C*. In which direction will it reflect?

7. What is the sign of the object-distance *u* when an object is placed before a concave mirror?

8. Where can the position of an object be if a concave mirror forms its erect and virtual image?

9. A mirror has focal length $f = +10$ cm. Is it convex or concave?

10. What are the values of the angle of incidence and the angle of reflection for normal incidence on a plane mirror? **(2005)**

11. In the diagram, the ray is incident parallel to the principal axis. Redraw the diagram, showing the reflected ray. **(2006)**

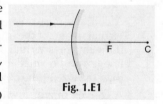

Fig. 1.E1

B. Short-Answer Questions

1. What is silvering of a mirror?

2. Write the two laws of reflection of light.

3. What do you understand by the radius of curvature of a spherical mirror?

4. What is the difference between a real image and a virtual image?

5. Draw a diagram showing the pole, focus, centre of curvature and principal axis of a concave mirror.

6. Convex mirrors are used as rear-view mirrors in scooters, motorcycles, etc. Explain why.

7. Draw ray diagrams to show the formation of images when an object is placed (a) between the pole and focus, and (b) between the centre of curvature and focus. **(2004)**

C. Long-Answer Questions

1. Describe a method to measure the focal length of a concave mirror.

2. Write the sign convention used for spherical mirrors.

3. By drawing a neat ray diagram, show the formation of the image of a point object placed above the principal axis of a convex mirror. Explain the construction.

D. Numerical Problems

1. An object is placed at a distance of 12 cm from a concave mirror of radius of curvature 16 cm. Find the position of the image.

2. An object of height 2 cm is placed at a distance of 15 cm from a concave mirror of focal length 10 cm. Draw a scale diagram to locate the image. From the diagram, find the length of the image formed.

3. The image of an object placed 16 cm from a concave mirror is formed at a distance of 24 cm from the mirror. Calculate the possible focal lengths of the concave mirror from this information.

4. An object is placed 20 cm from a convex mirror. Its image is formed 12 cm from the mirror. Find the focal length of the mirror.

5. Find the position, size and nature of the image formed by a spherical mirror from the following data.

   $f = -12$ cm,

   $u = -36$ cm,

   $h_o = 2$ cm

6. An object is placed at a distance of 12 cm from a concave mirror. The image formed is real and four times larger than the object. Calculate the distance of the image from the mirror. **(2006)**

7. An object is placed 24 cm from a concave mirror. Its image is inverted and double the size of the object. Find the focal length of the mirror and the position where the image is formed.

8. Where should an object be placed before a concave mirror of focal length 20 cm so that a real image is formed at a distance of 60 cm from it?

9. An object is placed at a distance of 12 cm from a convex mirror of radius of curvature 12 cm. Find the position of the image.

10. If the height of the object in the previous problem is 1.2 cm, what will be the height of the image?

11. When a concave mirror is placed facing the sun, the sun's rays converge to a point 10 cm from the mirror. Now, an erect, 2-cm-long pin is placed 15 cm away on the principal axis of the mirror. If you want to get the image of the pin on a card, where would you place the card? What would be the nature and height of the image?

E. *Objective Questions*

I. *Pick the correct option.*

1. A mirror forms a virtual image of a real object.
   (a) It must be a convex mirror.
   (b) It must be a concave mirror.
   (c) It must be a plane mirror.
   (d) It may be any of the mirrors mentioned above.

2. The angle of incidence is the angle between
   (a) the incident ray and the surface of the mirror
   (b) the reflected ray and the surface of the mirror
   (c) the normal to the surface and the incident ray
   (d) the normal to the surface and the reflected ray

3. The angle of reflection is the angle between
   (a) the incident ray and the surface of the mirror
   (b) the reflected ray and the surface of the mirror
   (c) the normal to the surface and the incident ray
   (d) the normal to the surface and the reflected ray

4. An object is placed at the centre of curvature of a concave mirror. The distance between its image and the pole is
   (a) equal to f
   (b) between f and $2f$
   (c) equal to $2f$
   (d) greater than $2f$

5. An object of size 2.0 cm is placed perpendicular to the principal axis of a concave mirror. The distance of the object from the mirror equals the radius of curvature. The size of the image will be
   (a) 0.5 cm (b) 1.0 cm
   (c) 1.5 cm (d) 2.0 cm

6. The magnification m of an image formed by a spherical mirror is negative. It means, the image is
   (a) smaller than the object
   (b) larger than the object
   (c) erect
   (d) inverted

7. A point object is placed on the principal axis of a spherical mirror. The object-distance u is
   (a) definitely negative
   (b) definitely positive
   (c) positive if the object is to the left of the centre of curvature
   (d) positive if the object is to the right of the centre of curvature

8. $f = \dfrac{r}{2}$ is valid
   (a) for convex mirrors but not for concave mirrors
   (b) for concave mirrors but not for convex mirrors
   (c) for both convex and concave mirrors
   (d) neither for convex mirrors nor for concave mirrors

9. A ray of light is incident on a concave mirror. If it is parallel to the principal axis, the reflected ray will
   (a) pass through the focus
   (b) pass through the centre of curvature
   (c) pass through the pole
   (d) retrace its path

10. If an incident ray passes through the centre of curvature of a spherical mirror, the reflected ray will
    (a) pass through the pole
    (b) pass through the focus
    (c) retrace its path
    (d) be parallel to the principal axis

11. To get an image larger than the object, one can use
    (a) a convex mirror but not a concave mirror
    (b) a concave mirror but not a convex mirror
    (c) either a convex mirror or a concave mirror
    (d) a plane mirror

II. *Mark the statements True (T) or False (F).*

1. Light cannot travel in vacuum.

2. No particle can ever move at a speed greater than that of light in vacuum.

3. The angle of incidence is equal to the angle of reflection. This is true for reflection from plane mirrors, but is not true for reflection from spherical mirrors.

4. The focal length of a spherical mirror has a smaller magnitude than that of its radius of curvature.

5. A spherical mirror never forms an image whose size is the same as that of the object.

6. A ray starting from the focus of a concave mirror becomes parallel to the principal axis after reflection.

7. The mirror equation is valid only if the aperture of the mirror is small.

8. A real image of a point object can be formed only by a concave mirror.

9. A ray of light incident parallel to the principal axis of a spherical mirror retraces its path after reflection.

· ANSWERS ·

D. *Numerical Problems*

1. 24 cm from the mirror, on the same side as the object.
2. 4 cm   3. 9.6 cm, 48 cm   4. 30 cm
5. 18 cm, 1 cm, real and inverted
6. 48 cm   7. 16 cm, 48 cm   8. 30 cm
9. 4 cm, behind the mirror   10. 0.4 cm
11. 30 cm from the mirror, real and inverted, 4 cm

E. *Objective Questions*

I. 1. (d)   2. (c)   3. (d)   4. (c)   5. (d)
   6. (d)   7. (a)   8. (c)   9. (a)   10. (c)
   11. (b)

II. 1. F   2. T   3. F   4. T   5. F
    6. T   7. T   8. T   9. F

❖

Refraction of Light

2

We know that light travels along straight lines. This is true as long as light travels in one medium, without encountering an obstacle. When light travelling in a medium (such as air) enters another medium (such as water), it generally bends at the surface separating the two media. But once it is in the second medium, it moves along a straight line. This phenomenon of bending of light at the surface separating two media is commonly known as refraction of light.

The surface separating the two media is also called the interface between them. Not all of the light incident on the interface between two media passes into the second medium after refraction. A small part of light gets reflected too. For most of our discussions on refraction, we shall neglect the reflected part.

As you would expect, refraction, or bending, of light changes the way we see things. A very common example is that of a spoon dipped in water. The parts of the spoon in air and water appear disjointed. While standing in a clear pool of water, the bottom looks raised and our legs appear shorter. Similarly, the bottom of a glass tumbler filled with water appears raised when viewed from above. If you put pins or coins in this tumbler and look from the side, their images appear enlarged. All these effects are due to refraction of light. Our ability to see also depends on refraction. Our eyes contain several transparent liquids. When light from an object enters our eyes, it is refracted at the surfaces of these liquids to produce an image. Refraction is also responsible for such wonderful things as the twinkling of stars and the sparkling of diamonds.

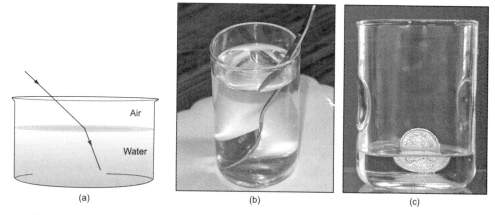

Fig. 2.1 (a) A ray of light bends, or refracts, as it enters a different medium. (b) Refraction of light is responsible for the bent image of the spoon. (c) It is also responsible for the enlarged image of the coin below water.

Refractive Index

Why does light bend when it enters a different medium? Does light bend by the same amount while entering different media? The answers to these lie in the fact that light travels at different speeds in different materials. Therefore, when it travels from one medium to another, it either speeds up or slows down. The amount by which its speed changes determines the amount by which it changes its direction.

You know that light travels at 299,792,458 m/s in vacuum. (This speed is often taken approximately as 300,000,000 m/s, i.e., 300,000 km/s.) The speed of light in a transparent medium such as glass, water or clear plastic is less than this. The ratio of the speed of light in vacuum to the speed of light in a medium is called the refractive index of the medium. This ratio is denoted by n or μ. Thus,

Refractive Index	$n = \dfrac{c}{v}$	...2.1

Here, c = the speed of light in vacuum and v = the speed of light in the medium.

In all material media the speed of light is less than c. Hence, the refractive index of a material medium is greater than 1 (see Table 2.1). The speed of light in air at atmospheric pressure is very close to that in vacuum, and we generally take the refractive index of air as 1 (the actual value is about 1.0003). The refractive index of water is about 1.33, and that of ordinary glass and diamond are about 1.50 and 2.42 respectively. Larger the refractive index of a medium, greater is the bending of light when it enters the medium from air obliquely. Thus light bends more when it enters a diamond than when it enters an imitation jewel made of glass.

Table 2.1 Refractive indices

Water	1.33
Kerosene	1.41
Benzene	1.50
Crown glass	1.52
Carbon disulphide	1.63
Flint glass	1.65
Diamond	2.42

EXAMPLE 2.1 A ray of light enters a diamond from air. If the refractive index of diamond is 2.42, by what per cent does the speed of light reduce on entering the diamond?

Solution   We have, $n = \dfrac{c}{v}$, where c is the speed of light in vacuum.

$\therefore$ the speed of light in diamond, $v = \dfrac{c}{n} = \dfrac{c}{2.42} = 0.41c.$

The speed of light in diamond is therefore 41% of its speed in air. In other words, in diamond, the speed reduces by 59%.

Laws of Refraction

The way a ray of light refracts when it is incident on the surface separating two media depends not only on the refractive indices of the media but also on the angle of incidence.

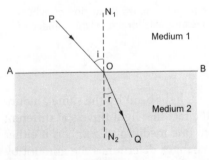

Fig. 2.2

Let AB represent a plane surface separating two transparent media—Medium 1 and Medium 2. Let their refractive indices be n_1 and n_2 respectively. The two media can be any pair such as air and water, or air and glass. Suppose a ray of light PO travelling in Medium 1 is incident on the surface AB at a point O. Draw a normal N_1ON_2 to the surface at O. ON_1 is in Medium 1 and ON_2 is in Medium 2. The angle i between the incident ray PO and the normal ON_1 is called the angle of incidence. The angle r between the refracted ray OQ and the normal ON_2 is called the angle of refraction. Two laws of refraction govern the refraction that takes place at a surface of separation such as AB.

	1. The incident ray, the refracted ray and the normal to the refracting surface at the point of incidence are in the same plane.
➤ Laws of Refraction	2. The angle of incidence and the angle of refraction satisfy the equation

$$\frac{\sin i}{\sin r} = \frac{n_2}{n_1} \qquad \ldots 2.2$$

The second law given above is also called Snell's law.

In the situation shown in Figure 2.2, if the first medium is air then $n_1 = 1$. Let the refractive index of the second medium be denoted by n. Equation 2.2 can then be written as

$$\frac{\sin i}{\sin r} = n \qquad \ldots 2.3$$

The ratio n_2/n_1 is also called the refractive index of Medium 2 with respect to Medium 1 and is denoted by the symbol n_{21}. If v_1 and v_2 are the speeds of light in Medium 1 and Medium 2 respectively,

$$n_{21} = \frac{n_2}{n_1} = \frac{c/v_2}{c/v_1}$$

or

$$n_{21} = \frac{v_1}{v_2} \qquad \ldots 2.4$$

Similarly, $n_{12} = \dfrac{v_2}{v_1}$. Thus, $n_{12} = \dfrac{1}{n_{21}}$.

EXAMPLE 2.2 A ray of light travelling in air falls on the surface of a transparent slab. The ray makes an angle of 45° with the normal to the surface. Find the angle made by the refracted ray with the normal within the slab. Refractive index of the material of the slab = $\sqrt{2}$.

Solution We have, $\dfrac{\sin i}{\sin r} = n$

or $\dfrac{\sin 45°}{\sin r} = \sqrt{2}$

or $\sin r = \dfrac{1}{\sqrt{2}} \times \sin 45° = \dfrac{1}{\sqrt{2}} \times \dfrac{1}{\sqrt{2}} = \dfrac{1}{2}$.

This gives $r = 30°$.

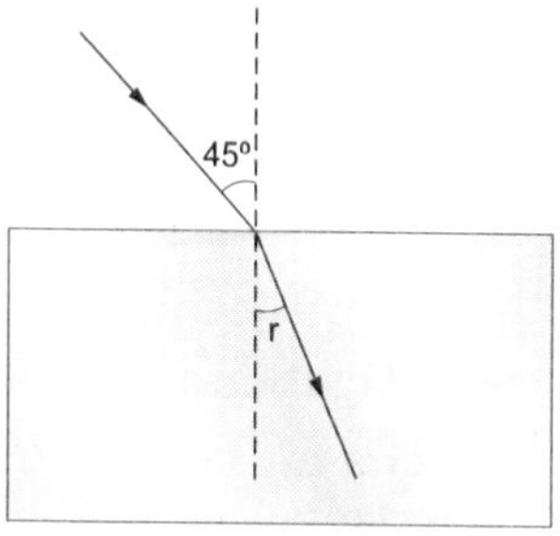

Fig. 2.3

If a ray falls perpendicularly on the refracting surface, it goes into the second medium without deviation. This is because in this case $i = 0$, and from Snell's law, $\sin r = (\sin i)/n = 0$, giving $r = 0$. For bending to take place, a ray has to fall obliquely on a surface separating two media of different refractive indices. Even though there is no bending in the case of normal incidence, we say that light has refracted. You can associate refraction with change in the speed of light as the medium changes, and that occurs even if the rays fall normally and proceed without bending.

Optically Denser and Rarer Media

Of a pair of transparent media, the one that has the higher refractive index is called the optically denser medium of the two, while the one that has the lower refractive index is called the optically rarer medium. Thus water and glass are optically denser than air, water is optically rarer than glass, and so on.

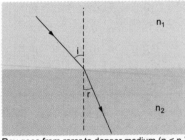
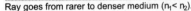

Ray goes from rarer to denser medium ($n_1 < n_2$).

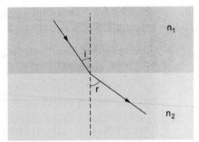

Ray goes from denser to rarer medium ($n_1 > n_2$).

Fig. 2.4

Remember that optically denser does not mean greater mass density (mass per unit volume). For example, kerosene is lighter than water (it floats on water), but it has higher refractive index, that is, it is optically denser than water.

When light goes from the optically rarer medium to the optically denser medium, it slows down and bends towards the normal. And when it goes from the denser medium to the rarer medium, it speeds up and bends away from the normal.

Put a coin in an opaque vessel placed on a table. Looking at the coin, move back your head till the coin just disappears from view. Then ask someone to pour water into the vessel gently, without displacing the coin. As the vessel fills with water, the coin will rise into view.

Figure 2.5 explains why this happens. Initially, the rays starting from the coin do not fall on the eye (Figure 2.5a). However, when the coin is below water, the rays bend at the surface of the water and fall on the eye (Figure 2.5b).

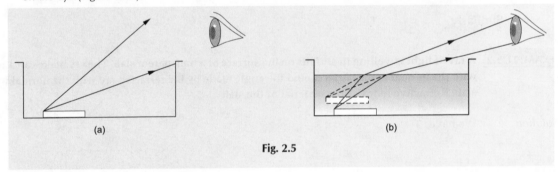

(a)   (b)

Fig. 2.5

Passage of Light through a Rectangular Slab

Let a ray of light RP travelling through air be incident on the upper surface of a transparent rectangular slab (Figure 2.6a). This ray gets refracted at the upper surface and moves along PQ within the slab. When it reaches the lower surface, it gets refracted again as it re-enters air. Figure 2.6b shows the cross section of the slab and the path of the ray.

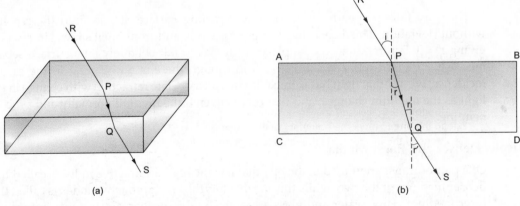

(a)   (b)

Fig. 2.6

For the refraction at P, let the angle of incidence and the angle of refraction be i and r respectively. If the refractive index of the material of the slab is n,

$$\frac{\sin i}{\sin r} = n. \qquad \qquad \ldots(i)$$

For the refraction at Q, PQ is the incident ray and QS is the refracted ray. Since AB and CD are parallel, the normals to them are also parallel. Hence, from geometry, the angle of incidence at Q is r. Let the angle of refraction be r'. Since for this refraction the slab is the first medium ($n_1 = n$) and air is the second medium ($n_2 = 1$), we have from Snell's law

$$\frac{\sin r}{\sin r'} = \frac{1}{n}$$

or $$\sin r' = n \sin r.$$

But from (i), $\sin i = n \sin r.$

∴ $$\sin r' = \sin i \qquad \text{or} \qquad r' = i.$$

This means that the ray QS is parallel to the ray RP. Thus, on passing through a transparent slab with parallel faces, a ray is displaced parallel to itself. That is, the ray is shifted laterally (sideways). The amount by which the ray is displaced is proportional to the thickness of the slab. Therefore, for a very thin slab (for example, a sheet of thin glass) the displacement is negligible.

Draw a thick, long line on a sheet of paper. Place a transparent rectangular glass or plastic slab on the line in such a way that the longer edges of the slab make an angle of about 45° with the line.

From different positions, look at the line through the slab. First look at it vertically from the top. The line below the slab will appear raised. Now look along the line from one side of the slab, with your eyes about the same level as the slab. The line on the other side of the slab will appear displaced (Figure 2.7b). This happens because the rays from the line get shifted sideways on passing through the slab.

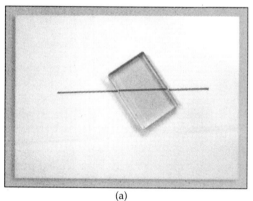

(a)

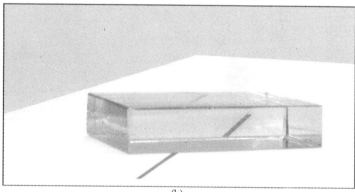

(b)

Fig. 2.7 Image of a straight line seen through different faces of a glass slab

Let us trace the path of a ray of light through a transparent glass slab. Fix a sheet of white paper on a board. Place the slab at its middle (Figure 2.8). Draw the boundary of the slab, and then draw a line RP to meet one of the longer boundaries at P, at an angle. Fix two pins A, B vertically on this line about 10 cm apart. Look at the image of the pins from the other side of the slab. Now fix a pin C such that it appears to be in a straight line with the images of A and B. Fix another pin D (at least 10 cm from C) such that all four pins appear to be in a straight line.

Remove the pins and join by a straight line the points where the pins C and D were inserted. Extend this line to meet the boundary of the slab at Q. Join PQ. The lines RP, PQ and QD represent the directions of the incident ray, the refracted ray within the slab and the emergent ray after the second refraction respectively.

You will find that the QD is parallel to RP. Also, it is shifted sideways from the direction of RP. Note that the incident ray bent towards the normal at P, as it moved from the optically rarer medium (air) to the optically denser medium (glass). At Q, the ray going from the optically denser medium (glass) to the optically rarer medium (air), bent away from the normal at Q.

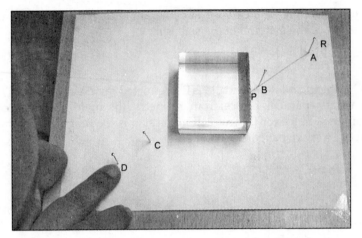
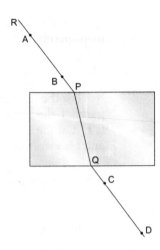

Fig. 2.8

You can repeat the experiment, once for the rays passing through the length of the slab and once, through its height. Verify that the lateral shift of the ray is proportional to the thickness of the material of the slab through which the ray passes.

Total Internal Reflection

Let a ray of light travel from a medium of higher refractive index (n_1) to a medium of lower refractive index (n_2), as shown in Figure 2.9a.

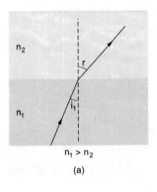
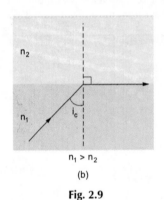
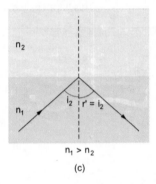

Fig. 2.9

After refraction, the ray of light bends away from the normal. Therefore, the angle of refraction is greater than the angle of incidence, i.e., $r > i$. Now, if the angle of incidence i increases, the angle of refraction r increases. For a particular value of i, called the critical angle (i_c), the angle of refraction becomes 90° (Figure 2.9b). The refracted ray then comes out parallel to the surface separating the two media. What happens for an angle of incidence greater than the critical angle? You would expect the angle of refraction to be more than 90°. This would bring the ray back into the first medium. But that would not be refraction. This means that for an angle of incidence greater than i_c, refraction is not possible. So, the ray reflects back into the first medium. This reflection obeys the laws of reflection, and therefore, $r' = i_2$ (Figure 2.9c). Such a reflection is called total internal reflection. Remember that total internal reflection takes place only for light travelling from a medium of higher refractive index to a medium of lower refractive index.

The total reflection of light travelling in a medium of higher refractive index when it is incident on the boundary with another medium of lower refractive index at an angle greater than the critical angle, is called total internal reflection.

Why 'total'? You know that when light falls obliquely on the interface between two transparent media, a small part of the light is reflected into the first medium. But when the angle of incidence is greater than the critical angle, the whole of the light gets reflected. Hence, it is called total internal reflection.

For $i = i_c$, $r = 90°$. From Snell's law,

$$\frac{\sin i}{\sin r} = \frac{n_2}{n_1} \quad \text{or} \quad \frac{\sin i_c}{\sin 90°} = \frac{\sin i_c}{1} = \frac{n_2}{n_1}$$

or

$$\sin i_c = \frac{n_2}{n_1}$$

...2.5

The critical angle is different for different pairs of media. The higher the refractive index (n_1) of the denser medium, the smaller is the critical angle for the pair.

Sparkling diamonds

The high refractive index (2.42) of diamond gives it a critical angle of only 24°. So, many rays trying to cross the diamond–air interface are incident at angles greater than the critical angle. The faces of the diamond are cut in such a way that most rays inside the diamond undergo total internal reflection. For example, most rays entering from the top of a properly cut diamond undergo multiple total internal reflections and emerge from the top face. But if we take a similarly cut piece of glass, a large number of incident rays emerge on the other side of the glass. Thus, the diamond sparkles in comparison, because the eye receives much more light from the diamond than it does from the glass.

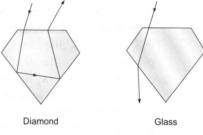

Diamond   Glass

Fig. 2.10

THIN LENSES

You have seen that when a ray of light passes through a transparent slab with parallel faces, the direction of the emergent ray remains the same as that of the incident ray. The ray just gets shifted sideways. What happens when light passes through a medium bounded by curved surfaces?

Cut two slits on a stiff piece of paper. Make it stand by fixing it over a window cut on one side of a cardboard box. Remove the opposite side of the box and let sunlight or torchlight fall on the slits to create 'rays'. Place a cylindrical tumbler filled with water in the path of the rays. You will find that the direction of the rays change after refraction. We use the refraction at a curved surface to make lenses.

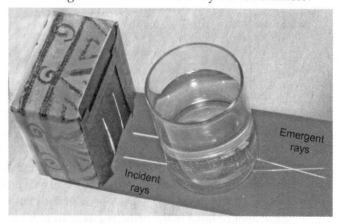

Fig. 2.11

A transparent material bounded by two surfaces of which at least one is curved is called a lens. Most lenses used in spectacles, magnifying glasses, cameras and microscopes have at least one spherical surface. In some cases, cylindrical lenses are used in spectacles. In this chapter we will study spherical lenses.

The cross sections of some lenses are shown in Figure 2.12. A lens that is thicker at the middle than at the edges is called a convex lens, while a lens that is thicker at the edges is called a concave lens. If someone in your family uses spectacles, find out by feeling the lenses whether they are concave or convex. If both the surfaces of a lens are convex, it is called a double-convex or biconvex lens. It is a type of convex lens. And the type of concave lens in which both the surfaces are concave is called a double-concave or biconcave lens.

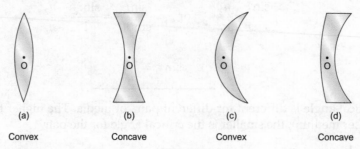

| (a) | (b) | (c) | (d) |
| Convex | Concave | Convex | Concave |

Fig. 2.12

Lenses of all kinds can be made very thin. Such lenses are called thin lenses. Figure 2.13 shows two thin lenses which have been divided into small sections. Notice that the middle section of each lens is almost rectangular. So, a ray of light incident on this section is displaced parallel to itself, and the displacement is proportional to the thickness of the section. For a thin lens, the displacement of a ray incident near its middle is negligible, and the ray passes through the lens almost without deviation. In our discussions we will assume that all the lenses are thin. Also, we will assume that the aperture (the surface of the lens) is small. Note that in the diagrams the width of the lens has been kept to give you a clear picture, and it does not indicate the actual thickness of the lens.

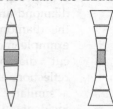

Fig. 2.13

Thin Lens Terms

Optical centre The central point O of the lens is called its optical centre (Figure 2.14). A ray incident towards the optical centre passes almost without any deviation through the lens.

Principal axis A lens is bounded by two spherical surfaces, and therefore, has two centres of curvature— C_1 and C_2. The line C_1C_2 joining them is called the principal axis of the lens.

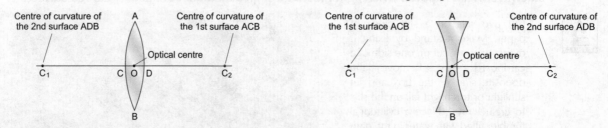

Fig. 2.14

Focus and focal length If a beam of light is incident parallel to the principal axis of a convex lens, it converges to a point F_2 on the principal axis on the *other side* of the lens (Figure 2.15a). This point is called the second principal focus of the convex lens. In case of a concave lens, a beam of light incident parallel to the principal axis diverges after passing through the lens (Figure 2.15b). If the transmitted rays are produced backwards, they meet at a point F_2 on the principal axis *on the side of the incident rays*. To an observer, the transmitted rays *appear* to come from this point. This point F_2 is called the second principal focus of the concave lens. In Figure 2.15c, a point object is kept at the point F_1 on the principal axis of a convex lens such that the rays starting from F_1 become parallel to the principal axis after transmission. Such a point is called the first principal focus of the convex lens. In Figure 2.15d, rays converging towards a point F_1 fall on a concave lens such that they become parallel to the principal axis after transmission. Such a point is called the first principal focus of the concave lens.

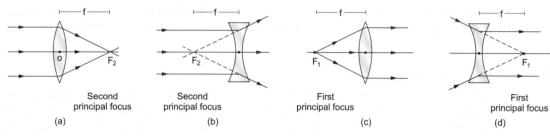

Fig. 2.15

If we stick to the convention that light is always incident from left to right on the lens, the first principal focus F_1 of a convex lens is on the left of the lens, and the second principal focus F_2 is on its right. For a concave lens, F_1 is on the right and F_2 is on the left of the lens.

For a thin lens, the distances of F_1 and F_2 from the optical centre are the same. This distance is called the focal length of the lens. Also, we usually use the word 'focus' for each of the two principal focii. It is generally clear from the situation whether we are talking of F_1 or F_2 and a common symbol F is used for them. Thus we can define the focus and focal length of a thin lens as follows.

In a thin lens, rays incident parallel to the principal axis after passing through the lens converge to or appear to diverge from a point on the principal axis. And, the rays coming from a point on the principal axis or rays going towards a point on it become parallel to the principal axis after passing through the lens. Each of these two points is called a focus of the thin lens, and the distance of the focus from the optical centre is called its focal length.

Usually, when we say 'focus', we mean the second principal focus.

Since a parallel beam of light incident on a convex lens converges on the other side, a convex lens is also called a converging lens (Figure 2.15a). On the other hand, a parallel beam of light incident on a concave lens diverges on the other side (Figure 2.15b). A concave lens is therefore also called a diverging lens.

Measuring the Focal Length of a Convex Lens

Take a convex lens (reading glasses use convex lenses). You can also use a magnifying glass. Face the lens towards the sun. Take a small block of wood and place it close to the lens such that the lens is between the sun and the block. Slowly move the lens away from the block. At one stage, a very small, bright image will be formed on the block. The distance between the lens and the block in this position is the focal length of the convex lens.

This method does not work for concave lenses. A concave lens forms a virtual image which cannot be captured on a screen such as your wooden block. Other methods are used to find its focal length.

Fig. 2.16

Power of a lens The power of a lens is defined as the reciprocal of its focal length.

$$P = \frac{1}{f}$$

...2.6

If focal length is measured in metres, power will be in metre^{-1}. This unit (metre^{-1}) is also called dioptre and is represented by D. Thus, if the focal length of a lens is 25 cm (that is, 0.25 m), its power will be

$$P = \frac{1}{0.25}\ \text{m}^{-1} = 4.0\ \text{m}^{-1} = 4.0\,\text{D}.$$

As we shall see, the focal length of a convex lens is taken as positive, whereas, that of a concave lens is taken as negative. So, the power of a convex lens is positive and that of a concave lens is negative.

Images Formed by Lenses

Consider a point object placed in front of a thin lens of small aperture. Light starting from the object travels in all directions. Those rays of light that fall on the lens are transmitted through the lens. The transmitted rays may actually intersect at a point, or they may intersect when produced backwards. Their point of intersection is the image of the object. If the rays actually intersect, the image formed is real. And if the rays intersect when produced backwards, the image formed is virtual. The image of an extended object can be found by locating the image of each point on it.

We can locate the image formed by a lens of a point object by tracing the paths of any two rays and finding their point of intersection. All transmitted rays will either pass through or seem to pass through this point of intersection. For convenience, we choose two rays whose paths are known. First, *we choose the ray that is incident parallel to the principal axis*. In case of a convex lens, the transmitted ray will pass through the focus, and in case of a concave lens, the transmitted ray's backward projection will pass through the focus. Then, *we choose the ray that passes through the optical centre of the lens*. This ray is transmitted without any deviation. The point of intersection of these two transmitted rays is the image of the point object. While tracing the rays, we do not show the ray bending at each surface of the lens. Instead, we show the incident rays getting bent at the central, vertical line of the lens.

Images formed by convex lenses

Figure 2.17 shows a typical case of image formation by a convex lens. AB is an object placed perpendicular to the principal axis of a convex lens. To locate the image of the point B, we draw two rays, BD and BO. The ray BD is parallel to the principal axis and passes through the focus F after transmission through the lens. The ray BO passes through the optical centre O and is transmitted without deviation. The transmitted rays DF and OB' intersect at B', which is the image of B. If we draw a perpendicular $B'A'$ to the principal axis, A' will be the image of A. Thus, $A'B'$ is the image of AB. In the case shown in Figure 2.17, the image $A'B'$ is real.

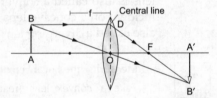

Fig. 2.17

Table 2.2 shows the ray diagrams for several cases of image formation by a convex lens. The object AB is placed perpendicular to the principal axis. The distance $OF_2 = OF_1$ is the focal length f. In the figures of this table, $2F_2$ denotes a point on the same side as F_2, at a distance $2f$ from O. Similarly, $2F_1$ denotes a point on the side of F_1, at a distance $2f$ from O.

Description In (a), the object is at infinity. So, the incident rays are parallel. The transmitted rays meet at the focus F_2, where a point-sized, real image is formed. As the object is brought closer, the image moves away from the lens, and its size starts increasing from the point-sized image formed at the focus. The image is real and inverted. But as long as the object is beyond $2F_1$, the size of the image is less than that of the object. This is shown in (b). When the object is at $2F_1$, i.e., at a distance $2f$ from the lens, the image is formed at the same distance on the other side, at $2F_2$. This image is of the same size as the object. This is shown in (c). When the object is between $2F_1$ and F_1, the image forms beyond $2F_2$, and its size is larger than that of the object. This is shown in (d).

What happens when the object is at the focus F_1? The ray diagram is shown in (e). The rays coming from B become parallel after transmission. We can say that the transmitted rays intersect at infinity, and hence, form a real image. Also, this image is below the principal axis. Thus, the image of AB is said to be inverted, real and infinitely large. However, to the eye in the path of the transmitted rays, the rays appear to be coming from a point at infinity on the side of incident rays. Therefore, from the observer's point of view, the image is virtual, erect and infinitely large.

If the object is placed between F_1 and O, i.e., within the focal length, a virtual, erect and enlarged image is formed, as shown in (f).

Table 2.2 Images formed by a convex lens

	Position of the object	Position of the image	Nature and size
(a)	at infinity	at F_2	real, point-sized
(b)	between infinity and $2F_1$	between F_2 and $2F_2$	real, smaller, inverted
(c)	at $2F_1$	at $2F_2$	real, same-sized, inverted
(d)	between $2F_1$ and F_1	between $2F_2$ and infinity	real, enlarged, inverted
*(e)	at F_1	at infinity	real, infinitely large, inverted
(f)	between F_1 and O	on the side of the object	virtual, larger, erect

* One can also say that the image is formed on the side of the object, and is virtual and erect. In fact, this is more practical from the observer's point of view.

EXAMPLE 2.3   **A convex lens forms a real and inverted image of an object. The size of the image is the same as that of the object. Where is the object placed?**

Solution   This situation is shown at (c) in Table 2.2. The object is placed at $2F_1$, that is, at twice the focal length from the lens.

....

Images Formed by a Concave Lens

Figure 2.18 shows the ray diagram of an image formed by a concave lens. The image is formed between the optical centre and the focus, and it is always virtual, erect and smaller than the object, for all positions of a real object. Table 2.3 summarizes image formation by a concave lens.

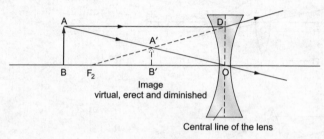

Fig. 2.18

Table 2.3   Images formed by a concave lens

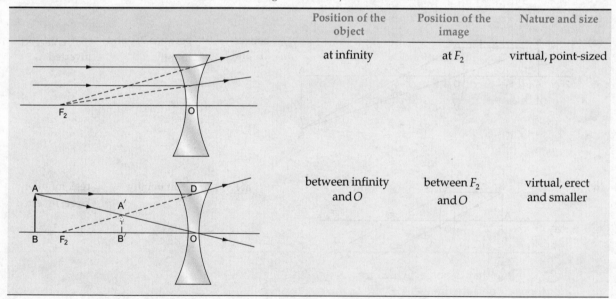

	Position of the object	Position of the image	Nature and size
	at infinity	at F_2	virtual, point-sized
	between infinity and O	between F_2 and O	virtual, erect and smaller

In this activity we will use the convex lens of a magnifying glass. First find the approximate focal length (*f*) of the lens. Then fix it vertically on a stand. Draw a long straight line on a table and place the lens stand on it. The principal axis of the lens should be parallel to and exactly above the line on the table. On one side of the stand mark the points F_1 and $2F_1$ on the line, at distances *f* and *2f* respectively from the lens. Similarly, mark F_2 and $2F_2$ one the other side of the stand.

Make a small screen of stiff paper and fix it on another stand. The screen should be vertical, with its centre at about the same height as the principal axis of the lens. Place the screen stand on the line drawn on the table.

Light a candle and place it on the line such that the lens is between the candle and the screen. The flame of the candle should be at about the same height as the principal axis of the lens. Move the screen back and forth till you see a sharp image of the flame on the screen. Repeat this by placing the candle at different positions. In each case note the size of the image. Also, note whether the image is erect or inverted. Try to verify all the entries of Table 2.2. In which cases are images not formed on the screen?

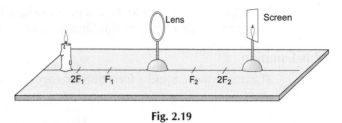

Fig. 2.19

Sign Convention

While discussing or working with thin lenses, we need three distances parallel to and two perpendicular to the principal axis. Corresponding to each of these distances we define a particular quantity and give it a symbol. These are given in Table 2.4.

Table 2.4

Distance	Quantity	Symbol
From the optical centre to the foot of the perpendicular drawn from the point object to the principal axis	object-distance	u
From the optical centre to the foot of the perpendicular drawn from the image of a point object to the principal axis	image-distance	v
From the optical centre to the second principal focus	focal length	f
Height of the object	object-height	h_o
Height of the image	image-height	h_e

The quantities u, v, f, h_o, h_e may be positive or negative. The rules for determining the signs of different quantities in coordinate convention are similar to those in the case of a mirror.

> **Coordinate Convention**
> - *u, v and f are measured from the optical centre.*
> - *If a distance is measured along the incident rays, the corresponding quantity is positive. If a distance is measured opposite to the incident rays, the corresponding quantity is negative.*
> - *The object-height h_o is always taken as positive. The image-height h_e is positive if the image and the object are on the same side of the principal axis. If the two are on the opposite sides of the principal axis, h_e is negative.*

Note that the object-distance u is negative for all cases of a real object. At (b) in Table 2.2, the focus F_2 and the image $A' B'$ are to the right of the lens. The distances OA' and OF_2 are measured along the incident rays. Thus v and f are positive.

At (f) in Table 2.2, OA' is measured from right to left, that is, opposite to the incident rays. Thus v is negative. The distance OF_2 is along the incident rays. So, f is positive. In Figure 2.18, the focus F_2 is to the left of the lens. The distance OF_2 in this case is measured opposite to the incident rays. Thus, f is negative.

The focal length of a convex lens is always positive and that of a concave lens is always negative in this convention.

As in the case of spherical mirrors, you can think of the principal axis as the x-axis and the optical centre as the origin. The object is, by convention, kept to the left of the lens, above the principal axis. The left-to-right direction is taken as the positive direction of the x-axis. The quantities u, v and f denote the x-coordinates of the object, the image and the focus respectively.

Since the object is kept to the left of the origin, its x-coordinate, i.e., u is negative. We can decide the signs of v and f also by thinking in terms of x-coordinates.

Lens Equation

The quantities u, v and f for a thin lens are related by the lens equation.

Lens Equation	$\dfrac{1}{v} - \dfrac{1}{u} = \dfrac{1}{f}$

...2.7

EXAMPLE 2.4   An object is placed 30 cm from a convex lens. A real image is formed 20 cm from the lens. Find the focal length of the lens.

Solution   By convention, the object is placed to the left of the lens. Hence, u is negative. Since the image is real, the transmitted rays actually intersect. The image is thus formed on the right of the lens as shown in Figure 2.20. Hence, v is positive. Thus,

$$u = -30 \text{ cm} \quad \text{and} \quad v = +20 \text{ cm}.$$

From the lens equation $\dfrac{1}{v} - \dfrac{1}{u} = \dfrac{1}{f}$ we have,

$$\frac{1}{f} = \frac{1}{+20 \text{ cm}} - \frac{1}{-30 \text{ cm}} = \frac{5}{60 \text{ cm}}$$

or $\quad f = 12 \text{ cm}.$

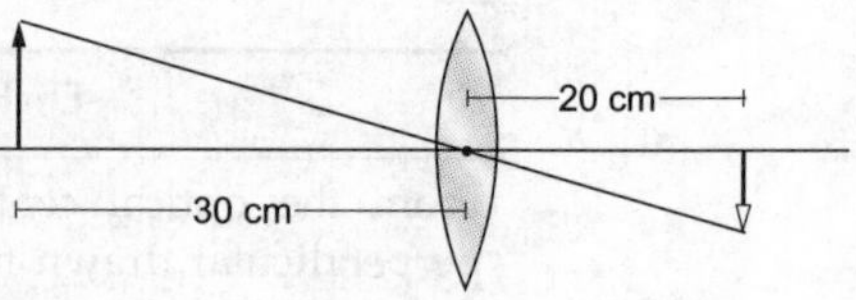

Fig. 2.20

Magnification

The image formed by a lens can be larger or smaller than the object, or it can be of the same size. If h_o and h_e denote the object-height and the image-height, the ratio h_e / h_o is defined as the magnification. It is denoted by the symbol m.

Magnification by a Thin Lens	$m = \dfrac{v}{u}$

...2.8

If m is positive, h_e is also positive. This means, the image and the object are on the same side of the principal axis (erect image). If m is negative, they are on the opposite sides of the principal axis (inverted image). For a convex lens, the image can be erect or inverted. When the image is erect (and virtual) the magnification is positive, and when the image is inverted (and real) m is negative. For a concave lens m is always positive.

Note the difference of sign in the equations for the magnification by a spherical mirror and the magnification by a thin lens.

EXAMPLE 2.5   A 2.0-cm-long pin is placed perpendicular to the principal axis of a convex lens of focal length 12 cm. The distance of the pin from the lens is 15 cm. Find the size of the image.

Solution   We have $u = -15$ cm and $f = +12$ cm (the signs of u and f are according to the sign convention).

We have $\qquad \dfrac{1}{v} - \dfrac{1}{u} = \dfrac{1}{f}$

or $\qquad \dfrac{1}{v} = \dfrac{1}{u} + \dfrac{1}{f}$

$$= \frac{1}{-15 \text{ cm}} + \frac{1}{12 \text{ cm}} = \frac{1}{60 \text{ cm}}$$

or $\qquad v = 60 \text{ cm}.$

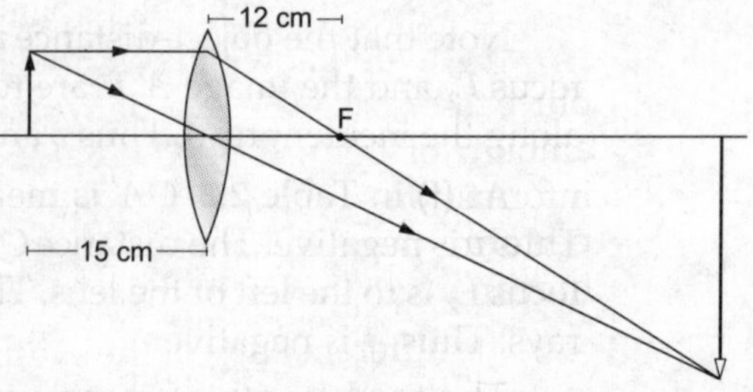

Fig. 2.21

The positive sign of v shows that the image is formed to the right of the lens, as shown in Figure 2.21. The magnification produced is

$$m = \frac{v}{u} = \frac{60 \text{ cm}}{-15 \text{ cm}} = -4$$

or $\quad \dfrac{h_e}{h_o} = -4$

or $\quad h_e = -4h_o = -4 \times 2.0\,\text{cm} = -8.0\,\text{cm}.$

The image of the pin is 8.0 cm high. The minus sign shows that it is formed below the principal axis, as shown in Figure 2.21. In other words, it is an inverted image.

Lenses in Contact

When two or more thin lenses are kept in contact with each other such that they have the same principal axis, the combination can be treated as a single thin lens. If the focal lengths of the individual lenses are $f_1, f_2,$, the focal length F of the equivalent single lens is given by

$$\frac{1}{F} = \frac{1}{f_1} + \frac{1}{f_2} + \dots$$

...2.9

For two lenses, this equation becomes $F = \dfrac{f_1 f_2}{f_1 + f_2}$.

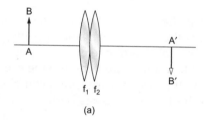 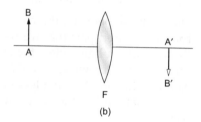

(a) (b)

Fig. 2.22

In Figure 2.22a, the two lenses in contact form an image $A'B'$ of AB.

In Figure 2.22b, the two lenses are replaced by a single lens of focal length $(f_1 f_2)/(f_1 + f_2)$. This lens also forms the image of AB at the same place $A'B'$. Equation 2.9 can also be written in terms of the powers of the lenses.

$$P = P_1 + P_2 + \dots$$

...2.10

This equation is often used in deciding the power of the lens to be prescribed for a person suffering from a defect of vision. If by putting two lenses of powers +2.0 D and +0.50 D in contact the person can see clearly, a lens of power +2.50 D is prescribed for that person.

THE EYE

Construction and Working

Now that you know the basics of image formation by lenses, you will be able to understand how our eyes work. The eye performs three functions: it makes adjustments to admit appropriate amount of light, it bends the rays of light to form a sharp image, and it collects and sends information about the image to the brain for further 'processing'. Different parts of the eye perform these functions. Figure 2.23a shows schematically the basic components of the human eye.

The different parts of the eye are contained within the spherical eyeball, which is about 2.5 cm in diameter. An opaque, white, protective membrane called the sclera covers most of the outer part of the eyeball. This is what we call the 'white of the eye'. A small portion at the front of the eyeball bulges out. A transparent protective membrane called the cornea covers this portion. Behind the cornea the major structures of the eye are the iris, which controls the amount of light entering the eye, the crystalline lens, which helps in bending light, and the retina, on which the image is formed. As you can see from the diagram, the lens divides the eye into two chambers. The smaller of these two is between the cornea and the lens. It is filled with a watery fluid called

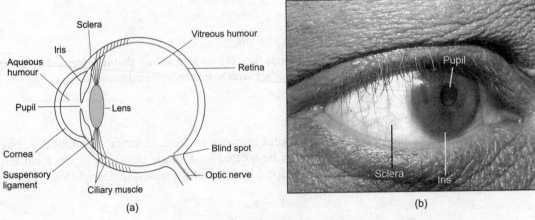

(a)   (b)

Fig. 2.23

the aqueous humour. The larger chamber, between the lens and the retina, is filled with jellylike fluid called the vitreous humour. This fluid helps in maintaining the shape of the eyeball. Now let us look at the functions of these structures in greater detail.

Light control Between the cornea and the lens lies a muscular diaphragm called the iris. The round, coloured part that we see in the eye is the iris. It has a small opening called the pupil, through which light enters the eye. The iris controls the diameter of the pupil automatically. In dim light, the iris widens (or *dilates*) the pupil to admit more light into the eye. In bright light, it contracts the pupil so that less light goes in. In this way, the iris–pupil combination controls the amount of light into the eye to ensure that the best-possible image is formed under different light conditions.

Formation of image Light is bent by refractions at the cornea and the lens such that a sharp image is formed on the retina. The crystalline lens is made up of jellylike, fibrous substances that make it elastic. The ciliary muscles, to which the lens is attached, can alter the curvature and thickness of the lens.

The average of the refractive indices of the materials of the lens is about 1.396. The liquids in front of and behind the lens have a refractive index of about 1.336. When light enters the eye from air, most of the bending occurs at the cornea itself because of the sharp change in refractive index. The difference in the refractive indices of the lens and the liquids surrounding it being smaller, light bends less at the lens. So, the lens just provides a kind of fine tuning.

The cornea–lens–fluid system is equivalent to a single converging lens, which we shall call the eye-lens. Since the ciliary muscles can change the curvature of the crystalline lens, it in effect can change the focal length of the eye-lens.

Sensing and passing on image information The image formed by the eye-lens on the retina is real, inverted and much smaller than the actual size of the object (Figure 2.24). The eye passes on image information to the brain. The brain processes this information to show us an erect image, which is much larger than that formed on the retina.

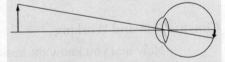

Fig. 2.24 The image formed on the retina is much smaller than the object.

To sense image information, the retina has two types of *sense receptors*. They are called rods and cones (named so because that is how they look under high magnification). There are about 10 million cones and 100 million rods on the retina. The rods can sense very small amounts of light, while the cones need more light to perform their task of sensing colours and details. That is why in dim light we are able to see shapes but not colours and details.

The rods and cones are actually the ends of special light-sensitive nerve cells. The long fibres (or axons) of these nerve cells come together at a point on the retina to form an optic nerve, which is connected to the brain. When light falls on the rods and cones, electrical signals are generated. These signals are transmitted to the brain via the optic nerves. There are no rods or cones at the spot where the optic nerve leaves the eyeball. If an image is formed on this region of the retina, it is not sensed, and hence, the object cannot be seen. This region is, therefore, called the blind spot of the eye. You can quite easily check for the existence of the blind spot in each eye. Cover your right eye and look at the triangle in Figure 2.25. Now slowly move the book towards your head. At a particular distance, the star on the left will disappear. At that distance light from the star is falling only on the blind spot of your left eye, and hence, you cannot see it. Now look at the star, with your left eye covered. At a particular distance, the triangle will disappear.

Fig. 2.25 Check out the blind spots in your eyes with the help of this picture. Find out how from the text.

Keep a glass of water on a table. Ask your friends to sit about 5–6 m from the table. Hold a coin in your hand and move it slowly near the glass. One by one your friends should cover one eye and say when the coin is just above the glass. When they say so, drop the coin. You will find that in most cases your friends judge the position of the coin wrongly, and the coin falls outside the glass. But if they look through both the eyes, they will be able to judge the position of the coin correctly most of the time, and the coin will drop into the glass. This happens because we are unable to judge depth, or the relative distances between objects, with one eye, especially when the objects are at some distance from the eye. *Two eyes are required to perceive depth. Also, we can see a wider area with two eyes than with one eye.*

How the Eye Adjusts for Objects at Different Distances: Accommodation

For clear vision, sharp images of objects have to form on the retina. Since the distance of the retina from the eye-lens is fixed, the image-distance v is fixed. However, we need to see objects that are at different distances from the eye. If you are looking at a cloud, the object-distance is large. If you are looking at your finger, the object-distance is small. To form clear and sharp images of both at the same distance from the lens, the focal length of the eye-lens has to change. As you know, the ciliary muscles can change the focal length of the eye-lens. When we are looking at a distant object (usually farther than 6 m), the ciliary muscles are in their most relaxed state. Then the focal length of the eye-lens is such that rays coming from the distant object are focused on the retina, and we see the object clearly (Figure 2.26a). When we are looking at a nearby object, the ciliary muscles contract to increase the curvature of the crystalline lens. The thickness of this lens increases, which decreases its focal length (and therefore, the focal length of the eye-lens). The ciliary muscles adjust the focal length in such a manner that a sharp image is formed on the retina (Figure 2.26b). This process of adjustment of the focal length of the eye-lens is called accommodation.

Accommodation is the process by which the eye changes the focal length of the eye-lens such that a sharp image is always formed on the retina.

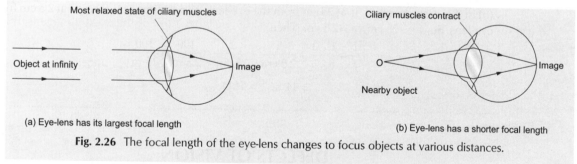

(a) Eye-lens has its largest focal length

(b) Eye-lens has a shorter focal length

Fig. 2.26 The focal length of the eye-lens changes to focus objects at various distances.

Far point and near point

Although the power of accommodation of the eye is amazing, it has certain limitations. The focal length of the eye cannot adjust enough to form sharp images of objects kept beyond a certain point and closer than a certain point. The farthest point up to which the eye can see properly is called the far point of the eye. For the normal eye, the far point is at infinity. When viewing an object at the far point, the ciliary muscles are in their most relaxed state, and the crystalline lens is at its thinnest (Figure 2.27a). Thus, the eye-lens is at its maximum focal length when looking at an object at the far point.

As an object is brought closer to the eye, the ciliary muscles contract. This increases the thickness of the crystalline lens and decreases the focal length of the eye-lens. This helps to form a sharp image on the retina. At a certain point near the eye, the ciliary muscles reach the limit of their contraction. If an object is brought closer still, the ciliary muscles cannot contract further. The closest point at which an object can be placed and seen clearly is called the near point of the eye. And, the distance of the closest point at which an object can be placed and seen clearly is called the least distance of distinct vision or the least distance of clear vision. When an object is placed at the near point (that is, at a distance equal to the least distance of distinct vision), the curvature and thickness of the crystalline lens are maximum and the focal length of the eye-lens is minimum (Figure 2.27b).

The near point of the eye varies from person to person and with age. At a very young age (below 10 years), the ciliary muscles are strong and flexible, and therefore, they can contract to a great extent. At this age, the near point may be as close as 7 to 8 cm from the eye. In old age, the ciliary muscles lose flexibility, and hence, the ability to contract to the required extent is lost . As a result, the near point recedes to 1 to 2 m, or even more. However, the standard value of the least distance of distinct vision for the normal human eye is taken as 25 centimetres.

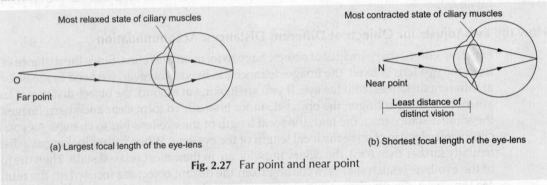

Fig. 2.27 Far point and near point

EXAMPLE 2.6 Calculate the power of the eye-lens of the normal eye when it is focused at its (a) far point (infinity) and (b) near point (25 cm from the eye). Assume the distance of the retina from the eye-lens to be 2.5 cm.

Solution (a) When the object is at infinity, the image forms at the focus of the lens ($v = f$). Hence, the focal length in this case is 2.5 cm. Thus, the power is

$$P = \frac{1}{f} = \frac{1}{2.5 \times 10^{-2} \text{ m}} = 40 \text{ D}.$$

(b) In this case, the object is at 25 cm from the eye-lens, and the image is formed at 2.5 cm from the eye-lens. So, $u = -25$ cm, $v = 2.5$ cm. Then

$$\frac{1}{f} = \frac{1}{v} - \frac{1}{u} = \frac{1}{2.5 \text{ cm}} + \frac{1}{25 \text{ cm}} = \frac{100}{2.5 \text{ m}} + \frac{100}{25 \text{ m}}$$

$$= 44 \text{ m}^{-1} = 44 \text{ D}.$$

DEFECTS OF VISION

As with any organ of the body, the eye can also develop problems. The inability to see nearby objects clearly and the inability to see faraway objects clearly are among the most common defects of vision.

Near-sightedness (Myopia)

Near-sightedness is a defect of vision due to which a person is not able to see distant objects clearly.

This defect is also called short-sightedness or myopia. It arises mainly due to two reasons.

(a) In certain people, the eyeball becomes elongated, i.e., longer than the normal eye. As a result, the distance of the retina from the crystalline lens increases. Then, even for the maximum focal length of the eye-lens, i.e., when the ciliary muscles are most relaxed, parallel rays of light from faraway objects get focused at a point before the retina (Figure 2.28a).

(b) In some cases, the curvatures of the cornea or the lens are such that the eye-lens has a shorter focal length (more power) than usual. In such cases also, the image forms short of the retina.

In both cases, faraway objects cannot be seen clearly, although nearby objects can.

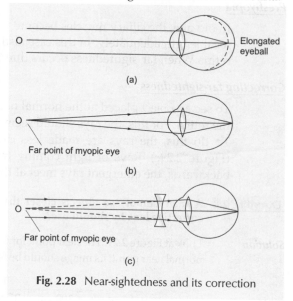

Though parallel rays focus short of the retina, a divergent beam coming from a point O gets focused on the retina, when the focal length of the eye-lens is maximum (Figure 2.28b). Then, for this person, O is the far point. Clearly, the far point of a myopic person is much closer than infinity.

Fig. 2.28 Near-sightedness and its correction

Correcting near-sightedness

To correct near-sightedness, a parallel beam is made divergent before it enters the eye, by putting a concave lens in front of the eye (Figure 2.28c). The focal length of the concave lens is so chosen that divergent rays entering the eye focus on the retina, and they appear to come from O—the far point of the unaided myopic eye.

EXAMPLE 2.7 A person suffering from myopia cannot see clearly beyond 1 m. What should be the focal length of the concave lens that will correct his vision?

Solution The situation is the same as that shown in Figure 2.28. The rays coming from a point O at a distance of 1 m from the eye, are focused on the retina. Parallel rays, after passing through the concave lens, should appear to come from O. By the definition of the focus of a concave lens, the point O is the focus of the concave lens used. So, the focal length of the concave lens should be 1 m.

Far-sightedness (Hypermetropia)

Some people cannot see nearby objects clearly, although they can see distant objects clearly. This defect is called far-sightedness, long-sightedness, hypermetropia or hyperopia. It arises mainly due to two reasons.

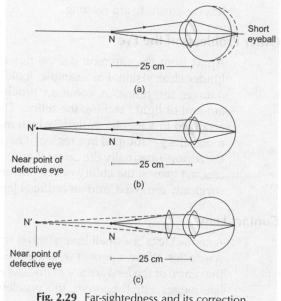

(a) In some people, the eyeball becomes shorter than the normal. As a result, the distance of the retina from the crystalline lens decreases. Then, even for the minimum focal length of the eye-lens, i.e., when the ciliary muscles are most contracted, the image of a nearby object is formed *behind* the retina (Figure 2.29a). Thus, nearby objects cannot be seen clearly.

(b) This defect can also occur if the eye-lens has a focal length that is larger than the normal due to abnormal curvatures of the cornea or the crystalline lens.

Fig. 2.29 Far-sightedness and its correction

People suffering from far-sightedness have difficulty in reading a book or a newspaper, or viewing a small object placed close to the normal near point, N (at 25 cm). People suffering from far-sightedness have to keep reading material or an object much farther away to see clearly. In other words, their near point, N', is farther than the normal near point, N (Figure 2.29 a and b).

Far-sightedness is a defect of vision due to which a person is not able to clearly see objects placed at the normal near point.

Presbyopia

In old age, the ciliary muscles become weak and are not able to contract enough to decrease the focal length adequately. In this case also, objects at the normal near point are not focused on the retina. When far-sightedness occurs due to this reason, it is called presbyopia.

Correcting far-sightedness

To see an object placed at the normal near point, N, clearly, its sharp image should be formed on the retina. For this, the rays should seem to be coming from N', the near point of the defective eye. To do this, the rays are made less divergent by placing a convex lens in front of the eye (Figure 2.29c). Rays of light coming from N pass through the convex lens. When produced backwards, the emergent rays meet at the point N'. Thus, a sharp image is formed on the retina.

EXAMPLE 2.8 A man cannot see objects closer than 1 metre from the eye clearly. What is the power of the corrective lens he should use?

Solution   Look at Figure 2.29. The near point for the man is 1 m from his eye. For him to see an object placed at the normal near point, its image should be formed 1 m from the eye. Here $v = -1$ m $= -100$ cm, $u = -25$ cm.

$$\frac{1}{f} = \frac{1}{v} - \frac{1}{u} = \frac{-1}{100\,\text{cm}} + \frac{1}{25\,\text{cm}} = \frac{3}{100\,\text{cm}} \quad \text{or} \quad f = \frac{100}{3}\,\text{cm} = \frac{1}{3}\,\text{m}.$$

Power of the lens, $P = \frac{1}{f} = \frac{1}{1/3}\,\text{m}^{-1} = +3$ dioptres.

A person may have any of the above defects or a combination of these defects. Among the elderly, the combination of near-sightedness and far-sightedness is common. Such people need converging glasses (convex lens) for reading and diverging glasses (concave lens) for seeing at a distance. They either keep two sets of spectacles or use bifocal lenses whose upper portion is for distant vision and lower portion is for reading. In many cases, both parts of the bifocal lens are concave. The upper part is highly divergent to correct near-sightedness and the lower part is kept less divergent to aid reading.

Other Problems of the Eye

Apart from the common defects described above, a person may develop other problems that hinder clear vision. For example, looking at the sun with naked eyes during a solar eclipse can damage the retina. A common problem in old age is cataract, which gradually reduces the amount of light reaching the retina. The crystalline lens of the eye is made of proteins that are arranged in a regular pattern, which makes the lens transparent. When a group of these protein molecules get lumped in a region, it becomes opaque, and we say that a cataract has developed in the region. Gradually the cataract grows, and finally, the whole lens becomes opaque. And as the cataract grows, the ability of the person to see diminishes. To restore vision, the affected lens is surgically removed, and an artificial lens is placed in its place.

Contact Lens

A contact lens is a small lens which is worn directly on the cornea. It has one clear advantage over spectacles. When a person wearing spectacles looks through the corner of the eye, the cornea and the centre of the lens are not in line. As a result, the peripheral view gets distorted. Since a contact lens moves with the cornea, this problem does not arise. Apart from this, some people may prefer contact lenses for cosmetic reasons.

Contact lenses require greater care than spectacles. They need to be stored and cleaned in the prescribed fashion. Improper use and maintenance of contact lenses can affect the cornea.

ATMOSPHERIC REFRACTION

You know that the earth is surrounded by a layer of air called the atmosphere. The density of air in the atmosphere is not the same everywhere. In general, it is greatest at the earth's surface and goes on decreasing as we move higher. The refractive index of air depends on its density—higher the density of air, greater its refractive index. Under standard conditions of temperature, humidity, etc., near the earth's surface, the refractive index of air is slightly greater than 1. It decreases with height, and is very close to 1 in the outermost region of the atmosphere.

The changes in refractive index of air give rise to many phenomena. For example, a rising current of hot air makes the objects viewed through it seem to flicker. You might have seen this happen as hot air rises above the heated surface of roads on hot summer days or above a large burning stove or *chulha*.

Hot air has less density, and hence, less refractive index than normal or cold air. At a point in the area above a hot surface, the refractive index keeps on changing as currents of hot air passes through it. So, the amount by which light passing through it is bent keeps on changing. This makes the objects viewed through this area seem to sway or flicker.

Early Sunrise and Late Sunset

Consider an oblique ray from a heavenly body such as the sun or a star. While travelling through the atmosphere, it continuously moves into regions of higher refractive index. So, it continuously bends towards the normal, resulting in a path similar to that shown in Figure 2.30. Since we see an object in the direction of the ray incident on the eye, the heavenly body appears higher than its actual position.

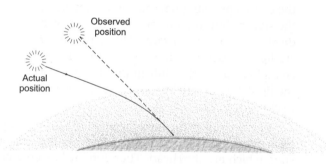

Fig. 2.30 Atmospheric refraction makes a heavenly body appear higher than its actual position.

Consider the situation when the sun just below the horizon (Figure 2.31). Rays of light coming from it get bent such that to an observer they seem to be coming from above the horizon. Thus, even when the sun's position is just below the horizon, the sun is visible to us. So, at sunrise we see the sun before it actually comes to the horizon. And at sunset we see it even after it has just dipped below the horizon. This increases daylight by about four minutes every day (two minutes at sunrise and two minutes at sunset).

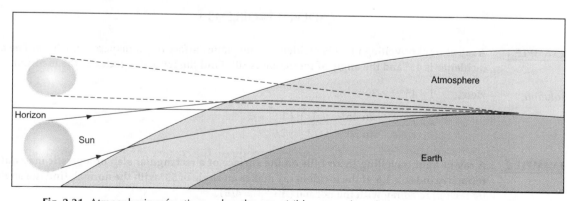

Fig. 2.31 Atmospheric refraction makes the sun visible even when the sun is just below the horizon.

You might have noted that the sun looks oval at sunrise and sunset. As you can see from the figure, the rays from the lower regions of the sun travel a greater distance through the atmosphere than those from the upper regions. So, they bend more. As a result, the image of the lower region gets shifted upwards more than that of the upper region. This makes the sun appear like a flattened circle, or an oval.

Twinkling of Stars

'Twinkle, twinkle little star' may have been the first rhyme you learnt, but maybe you are still wondering what makes stars twinkle. When we look at stars, quite often they do not appear to shine steadily. They disappear for a fraction of a second before reappearing (the intensity of light from them fluctuates), or their positions seem to shift slightly in random directions. We call this the twinkling of stars. Let us see why this happens.

Since the temperature of air and its humidity are not the same everywhere in the atmosphere, the refractive index of air varies between different masses (or pockets) of air, even at the same altitude. Thus, there exist air pockets whose refractive index is different from that of the air

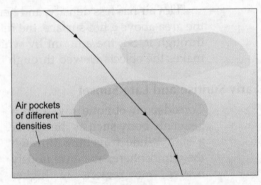

surrounding it. When a ray of light passes through such a pocket of air, it bends due to refraction (Figure 2.32). Light from a star may pass through one or more air pockets before reaching the eye. But the air pockets keep moving. So, the direction of the ray reaching the eye keeps changing, causing the image of the star to shift in random directions or even disappear for an instant. The amount of starlight reaching the eye also keeps changing due to the shift in the direction of the light. So, the brightness of the star seems to change.

Air pockets of different densities

Fig. 2.32

The stars near the horizon twinkle more than those that are overhead. This is because light from a star near the horizon has to cover much more distance in the atmosphere than that from stars which are overhead. Therefore, it has greater chances of encountering air pockets whose density is different from the surrounding air.

Why planets do not twinkle Planets do not seem to twinkle like stars, although light coming from them also passes through the air pockets in the atmosphere. This is because stars appear as point objects to us due to their enormous distance from the earth. On the other hand, planets are comparatively nearer, and therefore, for us they are more like extended objects. Light from different parts of the planet form an extended image at the eye, and we are unable to detect the random shifts in the smaller portions of this image.

· **SOLVED PROBLEMS** ·

EXAMPLE 1   A ray of light travelling in air is incident on the plane surface of a transparent medium. The angle of incidence is 45° and the angle of refraction is 30°. Find the refractive index of the medium.

Solution   Here, $i = 45°, r = 30°$.

$$n = \frac{\sin i}{\sin r} = \frac{\sin 45°}{\sin 30°} = \left(\frac{1}{\sqrt{2}}\right) \Big/ \left(\frac{1}{2}\right) = \sqrt{2}.$$

EXAMPLE 2   A ray of light travelling in air falls on the surface of a rectangular slab of a plastic material whose refractive index is 1.6. If the incident ray makes an angle of 53° with the normal, find the angle made by the refracted ray with the normal (sin 53° = 4/5).

Solution   The angle of incidence is 53° and the refractive index is $n = 1.6$.

We have, $\dfrac{\sin i}{\sin r} = n$ or $\dfrac{\sin 53°}{\sin r} = 1.6$

or $\sin r = \dfrac{\sin 53°}{1.6} = \dfrac{4}{5 \times 1.6} = \dfrac{1}{2}$ or $r = 30°$.

EXAMPLE 3 Find the refractive index of glass with respect to water. The refractive indices of these with respect to air are 3/2 and 4/3 respectively.

Solution We have, $n_{21} = \dfrac{n_2}{n_1}$. Here, glass is the second medium.

Here, $n_2 = \dfrac{3}{2},\ n_1 = \dfrac{4}{3}$.

So, $n_{21} = \dfrac{9}{8}$.

EXAMPLE 4 A point object is placed at a distance of 12 cm from a convex lens on its principal axis. Its image is formed on the other side of the lens at a distance of 18 cm from the lens. Find the focal length of the lens.

Solution According to convention, let the object be on the left of the lens. Therefore, u is negative, i.e., $u = -12$ cm. Since the image is on the other side, it is formed on the right of the lens. Thus, v is positive, i.e., $v = +18$ cm. (You can also say that since u is measured opposite to the direction of the incident rays, it is negative. And since v is measured along the direction of the incident rays, it is positive.)

We have $\dfrac{1}{f} = \dfrac{1}{v} - \dfrac{1}{u}$

or $\dfrac{1}{f} = \dfrac{1}{18 \text{ cm}} - \dfrac{1}{-12 \text{ cm}} = \dfrac{5}{36 \text{ cm}}$

or $f = \dfrac{36}{5}$ cm $= 7.2$ cm.

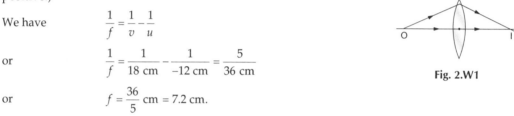

Fig. 2.W1

EXAMPLE 5 The image of an object formed by a convex lens is of the same size as the object. If the image is formed at a distance of 40 cm, find the focal length of the lens. Also, find the power of the lens. At what distance from the lens is the object placed?

Solution A same-sized image is formed when an object is placed at a distance of $2f$ from a convex lens. The image is formed at a distance of $2f$ from the lens. Here this distance is given as 40 cm. So,

$2f = 40$ cm or $f = 20$ cm.

Power, $P = \dfrac{1}{f} = \dfrac{1}{0.2 \text{ m}} = 5 \text{ D}$.

The object is placed at a distance of $2f = 40$ cm from the lens.

EXAMPLE 6 An object is placed on the principal axis of a concave lens at a distance of 20 cm from it. If the focal length of the lens is also 20 cm, find the location of the image.

Solution For a concave lens, f is negative. So, $f = -20$ cm. Since by convention the object is placed to the left of the lens, u is negative. Here, $u = -20$ cm.

We have $\dfrac{1}{v} - \dfrac{1}{u} = \dfrac{1}{f}$

or $\dfrac{1}{v} - \dfrac{1}{-20 \text{ cm}} = \dfrac{1}{-20 \text{ cm}}$

or $\dfrac{1}{v} = -\dfrac{1}{20 \text{ cm}} - \dfrac{1}{20 \text{ cm}} = -\dfrac{1}{10 \text{ cm}}$

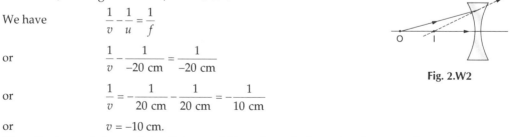

Fig. 2.W2

or $v = -10$ cm.

Thus, the image is formed at a distance of 10 cm from the lens. As v has turned out to be negative, the image must be on the left of the lens.

EXAMPLE 7   A beam of light travelling parallel to the principal axis of a concave lens appears to diverge from a point 20 cm behind the lens after passing through the lens. Find the power of the lens.

Solution   By definition, the point from where the beam appears to diverge is the focus of the lens. Thus, the focal length is 20 cm. As it is a concave lens, f is negative.

$$f = -20 \text{ cm} = -0.2 \text{ m}.$$

The power is $$P = \frac{1}{f} = \frac{1}{-0.2 \text{ m}} = -5 \text{ D}.$$

EXAMPLE 8   A convex lens of power 4 D is placed at a distance of 40 cm from a wall. At what distance from the lens should a candle be placed so that its image is formed on the wall?

Solution   Here, $f = \dfrac{1}{P} = \dfrac{1}{4 \text{ D}} = \dfrac{1}{4} \text{ m} = 25 \text{ cm}$, and $v = +40$ cm.

We have $$\frac{1}{v} - \frac{1}{u} = \frac{1}{f}$$

or $$\frac{1}{u} = \frac{1}{v} - \frac{1}{f} = \frac{1}{40 \text{ cm}} - \frac{1}{25 \text{ cm}} = -\frac{3}{200 \text{ cm}}.$$

So, the candle should be placed $\dfrac{200}{3}$ cm from the lens.

EXAMPLE 9   A pin which is 2 cm long is placed at a distance of 16 cm from a convex lens. Assuming it to be perpendicular to the principal axis, find the position, size and the nature of the image if the focal length of the lens is 12 cm.

Solution   Here, $u = -16$ cm and $f = +12$ cm.

We have $$\frac{1}{v} - \frac{1}{u} = \frac{1}{f}$$

or $$\frac{1}{v} = \frac{1}{u} + \frac{1}{f}$$

$$= \frac{1}{-16 \text{ cm}} + \frac{1}{12 \text{ cm}} = \frac{1}{48 \text{ cm}}$$

or $$v = +48 \text{ cm}.$$

The image is formed 48 cm from the lens on the side of the transmitted rays. The image is, therefore, real.

The magnification is $$m = \frac{v}{u} = \frac{48 \text{ cm}}{-16 \text{ cm}} = -3.$$

or $$\frac{h_e}{h_o} = -3$$

or $$h_e = -3h_o = -3 \times 2 \text{ cm} = -6 \text{ cm}.$$

The image is inverted and is 6 cm in size. So, an inverted and real image of size 6 cm is formed 48 cm from the lens.

EXAMPLE 10   A 4.0-cm-high object is placed at a distance of 60 cm from a concave lens of focal length 20 cm. Find the size of the image.

Solution   We have, $f = -20$ cm and $u = -60$ cm.

For a lens $$\frac{1}{v} - \frac{1}{u} = \frac{1}{f}$$

or $$\frac{1}{v} = \frac{1}{u} + \frac{1}{f}$$

$$= \frac{1}{-60 \text{ cm}} + \frac{1}{-20 \text{ cm}} = -\frac{1}{15 \text{ cm}}$$

or $$v = -15 \text{ cm}.$$

The magnification is $$m = \frac{h_e}{h_o} = \frac{v}{u} = \frac{-15 \text{ cm}}{-60 \text{ cm}} = \frac{1}{4}$$

or $$h_e = \frac{h_o}{4} = \frac{4.0 \text{ cm}}{4} = 1.0 \text{ cm}.$$

So, the image is 1.0 cm high. The positive sign shows that it is erect.

EXAMPLE 11 A convex lens of focal length 20 cm is placed in contact with a concave lens of focal length 12.5 cm in such a way that they have the same principal axis. Find the power of the combination.

Solution $P = P_1 + P_2$.

Here, $P_1 = +\dfrac{1}{20 \text{ cm}} = +\dfrac{1}{0.20 \text{ m}} = 5 \text{ D}$ and $P_2 = -\dfrac{1}{12.5 \text{ cm}} = -\dfrac{1}{0.125 \text{ m}} = -8 \text{ D}$.

So, the power of the combination is $P_1 + P_2 = -3 \text{ D}$.

· POINTS TO REMEMBER ·

- When light travelling in one medium falls at an angle on another medium, it bends. This phenomenon of bending of light at the surface separating two media is commonly known as *refraction of light*.

- The ratio of the speed of light in vacuum to the speed of light in a medium is called the refractive index (n) of the medium. $n = c/v$, where c and v are the speeds of light in vacuum and the medium respectively.

- *Laws of refraction*

  1. The incident ray, the refracted ray and the normal to the refracting surface at the point of incidence are in the same plane.

  2. The angle of incidence and the angle of refraction satisfy the equation

     $$\frac{\sin i}{\sin r} = \frac{n_2}{n_1}.$$

- Of a pair of transparent media, the one that has the higher refractive index is called the *optically denser medium* of the two, while the one that has the lower refractive index is called the *optically rarer medium*. When light goes from the optically rarer medium to the optically denser medium, it bends towards the normal. And when it goes from the denser medium to the rarer medium, it bends away from the normal.

- The total reflection of light travelling in a medium of higher refractive index (n_1) when it is incident on the boundary with another medium of lower refractive index (n_2) at an angle greater than the critical angle, is called *total internal reflection*. The critical angle is given by

  $$\sin i_c = \frac{n_2}{n_1}.$$

- When a ray of light passes through a transparent slab with parallel faces, it is displaced parallel to itself.

- A lens that is thicker at the middle than at the edges is called a *convex lens*, while a lens that is thicker at the edges is called a *concave lens*.

- The central point of a lens is called its *optical centre*. A ray of light incident towards the optical centre passes almost undeviated through the lens.

The line joining the two centres of curvature of a lens is called its *principal axis*. In a thin lens, rays incident parallel to the principal axis after passing through the lens converge to or appear to diverge from a point on the principal axis. This point is called the *second principal focus* of the thin lens. If the rays diverging from a point or converging towards a point become parallel to the principal axis after transmission through the lens, the point is called the *first principal focus* of the lens. The two principal focii are at the same distance from the lens and this distance is called its focal length.

- *Images formed by a thin lens*

  A convex lens can form real as well as virtual image. If the image is real, it is inverted. If the image is virtual, it is erect. The size of the image is smaller for objects beyond 2F, equal in size for objects at 2F, and larger in size for objects between 2F and the lens.

  A concave lens always forms a virtual, erect and smaller image.

- *Sign convention*

  The quantities u, v, f are defined corresponding to the distance of the object, image and the second focus from the optical centre. If a distance is measured along the incident rays, the corresponding quantity is positive. If a distance is measured opposite to the incident rays, the corresponding quantity is negative.

  The object-height (h_0) is always taken as positive. If the image is formed on the same side of the principal axis (erect image), the image-height (h_e) is also positive. If the image is formed on the opposite side (inverted image), h_e is negative.

  The focal length of a convex lens is positive, while that of a concave lens is negative.

- The power of a lens is defined as the reciprocal of its focal length. If f is in metres, power is in *dioptres* (metre^{-1}).

- *Eye*

  Light entering the eye is controlled by the size of the pupil, which can be changed with the help of the iris. In dim light, the pupil widens to allow more light to go in. In bright light, it contracts.

The light entering the eye is bent mainly at the cornea before falling on the crystalline lens at which a little additional bending takes place. The cornea–lens–fluid system of the eye is equivalent to a single converging lens—the *eye-lens*. The ciliary muscles contract and relax to change the overall focal length of the eye-lens so that sharp images of objects at different distances are formed on the retina. This process is called *accommodation*.

The retina has millions of receptors known as rods and cones. These receptors pass image information to the brain via an optic nerve connected to each eye. Rods are more numerous and work in dim light also. Cones gather information about colour and details, and need good light to work.

The farthest point up to which the eye can see properly is called the *far point* of the eye. The closest point at which an object can be placed and seen clearly is called the *near point*. And, the distance of the closest point at which an object can be placed and seen clearly is called the *least distance of distinct vision* or *least distance of clear vision*.

- *Defects of vision*

Near-sightedness is a defect of vision due to which a person is not able to see distant objects clearly. It is also called *short-sightedness* or *myopia*.

Far-sightedness is a defect of vision due to which a person is not able to clearly see objects placed at the normal near point. It is also called *long-sightedness, hypermetropia* or *hyperopia*.

Near-sightedness can be corrected with a concave lens and far-sightedness, with a convex lens.

Contact lenses are small lenses worn directly on the cornea. Unlike spectacles, they do not distort peripheral vision.

- *Atmospheric refraction*

Atmospheric refraction is responsible for a number of optical phenomena such as the twinkling of stars and the appearance of a heavenly body higher than its actual position.

- *Mathematical relations*

For a thin lens	$\dfrac{1}{v} - \dfrac{1}{u} = \dfrac{1}{f}$
Magnification by a thin lens	$m = \dfrac{h_e}{h_o} = \dfrac{v}{u}$
Power of a thin lens	$P = \dfrac{1}{f}$

· EXERCISES ·

A. *Very-Short-Answer Questions*

1. Define refractive index.

2. When a ray of light passes from Medium 1 to Medium 2, it bends away from the normal. Which of the two is the optically denser medium?

3. A ray of light travelling in air is incident on a face of a rectangular slab and comes out from the opposite face. The angle between the incident ray and the normal to the surface is 30°. What is the angle between the ray coming out of the slab and the normal to the face from which it comes out?

4. How should a ray be incident on a rectangular slab so that it comes out from the opposite side without being displaced?

5. Define the principal axis of a lens.

6. Where should an object be placed before a convex lens so that a real image of the same size as the object is formed?

7. Where should a pin be placed before a convex lens so that the image formed is at infinity?

8. The focal length of a thin lens is given by $f = -10$ cm. Is the lens concave or convex?

9. The power of a lens used in the reading glasses of a person is +1.5 D. Is the lens concave or convex?

10. When an object is placed before a lens, the lens forms a virtual image for all positions of the object. Is the lens convex or concave?

11. A lens forms an erect image for all positions of an object in front of it. Is the lens convex or concave?

12. Write the relation between u, v and f of a thin lens.

13. Name the muscles responsible for the focusing mechanism of the eye.

14. Name the sense receptors found on the retina of the eye.

15. Define the following in one sentence each.
    (a) Near point of the eye
    (b) Far point of the eye
    (c) Least distance of distinct vision
    (d) Accommodation

16. Name two common defects of the eye.

17. What kind of lens should be given to a person suffering from near-sightedness (myopia)?

18. A person has concave lenses in his spectacles. Which defect of vision is he suffering from?

19. Which kind of lens is used to correct long-sightedness (hypermetropia)?

20. A student sitting at the back of a class is not able to see what is written on the blackboard. What defect of vision is he suffering from? Which lens (convex or concave) should be used to correct the defect?

21. What is the main advantage of a contact lens over spectacles?

B. Short-Answer Questions

1. Write Snell's law, explaining the meaning of the symbols used.

2. What is a thin lens? What is the difference in construction between a convex and a concave lens?

3. Why is a convex lens called a converging lens and a concave lens, a diverging lens?

4. How do you conclude that a ray of light incident towards the optical centre of a thin lens is transmitted almost without any deviation?

5. The focal length of a convex lens is f. How does the size of the image placed in front of it changes as the object is brought progressively closer to the focus from a distance which is just greater than $2f$?

6. Assuming the principal axis as the x-axis and the optical centre as the origin, how will you determine the signs of the quantities u, v and f for a lens?

7. Draw a neat diagram of the human eye and indicate its main parts.

8. How does the eye control the amount of light entering it?

9. What is the blind spot of the eye?

10. Why can you not see an object clearly if it is placed very close to your eyes?

11. Why do planets not appear to twinkle like stars?

C. Long-Answer Questions

1. An extended object is placed perpendicular to the principal axis of a convex lens. Draw neat diagrams to show the image formation in the following cases. (a) The object is at a distance that is more than double the focal length of the lens. (b) The object is at a distance equal to double the focal length. (c) The object is at a distance that is more than its focal length but is less than double the focal length.

2. Describe a method to measure the focal length of a convex lens.

3. Explain the process of accommodation in the human eye.

4. What is myopia (near-sightedness)? Explain with a ray diagram how it can be corrected using a lens.

5. What is hypermetropia (far-sightedness)? Write two causes for the development of this defect. Explain how it can be corrected using a lens. (2005, '06)

6. Describe briefly why stars twinkle.

7. Why does the sun become visible even before it actually rises above the horizon at sunrise?

D. Numerical Problems

1. The refractive indices of water and glass are 4/3 and 3/2 respectively. Find the speed of light in each. (Similar, 2005)

2. A ray of light travelling in air falls on the surface of a transparent material at an angle of 45° to the normal. It bends by 15° after refraction. Find the refractive index of the material.

3. A ray of light travelling in air is incident on the surface of a plastic slab at an angle. If the angle of refraction is 30°, and the refractive index of the plastic is $\sqrt{3}$, find the angle of incidence.

4. Light is incident on a clear-plastic block at an angle of 45°. The speed of light in the plastic is $c/\sqrt{2}$, where c is the speed of light in vacuum. Find the angle of refraction.

5. Find the refractive index of air with respect to water ($n_{water} = \frac{4}{3}$).

6. A diamond ($n = 2.42$) is dipped in a liquid of refractive index 1.4. Find the refractive index of diamond with respect to the liquid.

7. An object is placed at a distance of 30 cm from a convex lens of focal length 20 cm.
   (a) Find the position of the image.
   (b) Is the image real or virtual?
   (c) Is the image erect or inverted?

8. A 1.0-cm-high object is placed at a distance of 12 cm from a convex lens of focal length 16 cm.
   (a) Find the position of the image.
   (b) Is the image real or virtual?
   (c) Find the size of the image.
   (d) Is the image erect or inverted? (Similar, 2004)

9. A 2.0-cm-high object is placed 12 cm from a convex lens, perpendicular to its principal axis. The lens forms a real image, whose size is 1.5 cm. Find the power of the lens.

10. An object is placed at a distance of 10 cm from a concave lens of focal length 20 cm. Find the position of the image and discuss its nature.

11. A 3.5-cm-high object is placed at a distance of 12 cm from a concave lens of focal length 16 cm. Find the size of the image.

12. An object is placed at a distance of 50 cm from a concave lens. The image is formed at a distance of 20 cm from the lens. Find the focal length of the lens.

13. An object is placed before a concave lens of focal length 12 cm. The size of the image formed by the lens is half the size of the object. Calculate distance of the object from the lens.

14. What is the power of a concave lens of focal length 50 cm?

15. A convex lens of focal length 18 cm and a concave lens of focal length 24 cm are placed in contact such that they have a common principal axis. Will the combination act as a convex lens or a concave lens? Find the focal length and power of the combination.

16. The far point of a person suffering from myopia is 2 metres from the eye. Find the focal length and power of the corrective lens that will correct his vision.

17. The near point of an elderly person is 50 cm from the eye. Find the focal length and power of the corrective lens that will correct his vision.

E. *Objective Questions*

I. *Pick the correct option.*

1. A ray of light travelling in air falls obliquely on the surface of a calm pond. It will
   (a) go into the water without deviating from its path
   (b) deviate away from the normal
   (c) deviate towards the normal
   (d) turn back on its original path

2. A ray of light goes from a medium of refractive index n_1 to a medium of refractive index n_2. The angle of incidence is i and the angle of refraction is r. Then, $\sin i / \sin r$ is equal to
   (a) n_1 (b) n_2 (c) n_1/n_2 (d) n_2/n_1

3. A thin lens and a spherical mirror have a focal length of +15 cm each.
   (a) Both are convex.
   (b) The lens is convex and the mirror is concave.
   (c) The lens is concave and the mirror is convex.
   (d) Both are concave.

4. A convex lens
   (a) is thicker at the middle than at the edges
   (b) is thicker at the edges than at the middle
   (c) has uniform thickness everywhere
   (d) is called a diverging lens

5. A convex lens forms a virtual image when an object is placed at a distance of 18 cm from it. The focal length must be
   (a) greater than 36 cm   (b) greater than 18 cm
   (c) less than 36 cm   (d) less than 18 cm

6. An object is placed before a convex lens. The image formed
   (a) is always real   (b) may be real or virtual
   (c) is always virtual   (d) is always erect

7. An object is placed before a concave lens. The image formed
   (a) is always erect
   (b) may be erect or inverted
   (c) is always inverted
   (d) is always real

8. A lens has a power of +0.5 D. It is
   (a) a concave lens of focal length 5 m
   (b) a convex lens of focal length 5 cm

   (c) a convex lens of focal length 2 m
   (d) a concave lens of focal length 2 m

9. A parallel beam of light falling on the eye gets focused on the retina because of refractions at
   (a) the cornea
   (b) the crystalline lens
   (c) the vitreous humor
   (d) various surfaces in the eye

10. The combination responsible for admitting different amounts of light into the eye is
    (a) ciliary muscles and crystalline lens
    (b) ciliary muscles and pupil
    (c) iris and pupil
    (d) rods and cones

11. The muscles of the iris control the
    (a) focal length of the eye-lens
    (b) opening of the pupil
    (c) shape of the crystalline lens
    (d) optic nerve

12. When the eye is focused on an object very far away, the focal length of the eye-lens is
    (a) maximum
    (b) minimum
    (c) equal to that of the crystalline lens
    (d) half its maximum focal length

13. Other names for myopia are
    (a) hyperopia and hypermetropia
    (b) long-sightedness and hyperopia
    (c) near-sightedness and presbyopia
    (d) near-sightedness and short-sightedness

14. The inability among the elderly to see nearby objects clearly because of the weakening of the ciliary muscles is called
    (a) far-sightedness   (b) near-sightedness
    (c) presbyopia   (d) myopia

II. *Mark the statements True (T) or False (F).*

1. When a ray of light passes from an optically denser medium to a rarer medium, it slows down.

2. If a ray of light passes from vacuum to a transparent medium, it will bend away from the normal.

3. The central portion of a thin lens behaves like a rectangular slab.

4. The values of f and u for a concave lens are always negative by convention.

5. When two lenses are placed in contact, the focal length of the combination is equal to the sum of the focal lengths of the lenses.

6. The number of cones in the human eye is more than the number of rods.

7. When light rays are incident on the eye, maximum deviation takes place at the cornea.

8. For the myopic eye, the far point is farther away than normal.

· ANSWERS ·

D. *Numerical Problems*

1. 2.25×10^8 m/s, 2×10^8 m/s   2. $\sqrt{2}$ 3. $60°$

4. $30°$ 5. $3/4$ 6. 1.73

7. (a) 60 cm from the lens on the other side
   (b) real (c) inverted

8. (a) 48 cm on the object side (b) virtual
   (c) 4.0 cm (d) erect

9. $(175/9)$ D

10. 6.67 cm on the object side; virtual, erect and
    smaller than the object

11. 2 cm   12. 33.3 cm   13. 12 cm   14. -2 D

15. convex, 72 cm, $(25/18)$ D   16. 2 m, -0.5 D

17. 50 cm, $+2$ D

E. *Objective Questions*

I.   1. (c)   2. (d)   3. (a)   4. (a)   5. (b)

      6. (b)   7. (a)   8. (c)   9. (d)   10. (c)

      11. (b)   12. (a)   13. (d)   14. (c)

II.   1. F   2. F   3. T   4. T   5. F

       6. F   7. T   8. F

❖

Dispersion and Scattering of Light

DISPERSION OF LIGHT

We see colours all around us. The blue sky, green leaves, red roses, yellow sunflowers, colourful birds and butterflies, etc., are just some of the colours we see in nature. And then we have the colours of our clothes, pens, pencils, houses, vehicles, and so on. The colours we see depend on the colour of light entering our eyes from an object or a source of light. Different sources of light may produce lights of different colours. A sodium-vapour lamp, for example, produces a yellowish light. The flame of a gas stove emits blue light. But sunlight does not appear to have a colour. The same is true of certain types of bulbs we use at home. We call such light (i.e., those that appear colourless) white light.

Though white light does not appear coloured, it is actually a mixture of lights of different colours present in a definite proportion. Lights of different colours have different wavelengths. So, they behave differently. For example, they travel at different speeds. This makes the refractive index of a transparent material slightly different for different colours of lights. So, lights of different colours bend by different amounts on refraction. Therefore, under certain conditions, when white light gets refracted, its components bend by different amounts and separate out. You must have seen this happen when sunlight passing through a glass of water falls on the table or the floor, producing a band of colours. The phenomenon of splitting of light into its component colours due to the dependence of refractive index on wavelength is called the dispersion of light.

Prism

Quite often we use a glass prism to split white light. A glass prism is a five-sided solid with a triangular cross section. Thus, it has two parallel, triangular faces and three rectangular faces that are inclined to each other. In experiments, a prism is usually placed on one of its triangular faces such that its rectangular faces are vertical. Light falling on a rectangular face (*adfc* in Figure 3.1) enters the prism and emerges from another rectangular face (*befc*).

Figure 3.2 shows the cross section of a prism on which a ray of light PQ is incident. The ray PQ makes an angle i_1 with the normal to the surface at Q. Since the ray enters glass (optically denser medium) from air, it bends towards the normal. Hence, the ray bends towards the base AB. Within the prism, the ray travels along QR, and falls on the surface CB at R. At this surface, the ray passes from glass to air, and hence, it bends away from the normal. As a result, the ray bends further towards the base AB. Note that for the refraction at the second surface in a prism, it is a convention to denote the angle of incidence by r_2 and the angle of refraction by i_2.

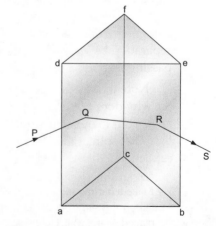

Fig. 3.1 A ray of light passing through a prism

You know that when a ray of light passes through a transparent rectangular slab with parallel faces, the emergent ray gets displaced parallel to itself. But a prism causes a net deviation (change in direction) in the path of a ray of light. In Figure 3.2, if the prism were not present, the ray of light would have travelled along a straight line, i.e., along PT. Because of the refractions at the two surfaces of the prism, the ray bends and travels along RS after emerging from the prism. The total angle through which the ray deviates is $\delta = \angle TDS$. This angle (δ) is called the angle of deviation. For a given angle of

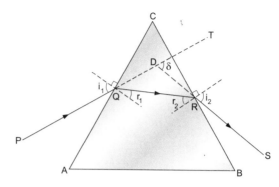

Fig. 3.2 Cross section of a prism showing passage of a ray

incidence i_1, the deviation δ produced by a prism depends on the refractive index of the prism material. The higher the refractive index, the greater is the deviation.

Let us trace a ray of light through a prism. Fix a sheet of white paper on a board. Place the prism on it and draw its outline ABC. Draw a line PQ that meets AC at Q, at an angle of about 30° to AC. Fix two pins K and L vertically on this line, about 10 cm apart. Now look at the image of the pins from the side BC of the prism. Fix a pin M such that it appears to be in a straight line with the images of K and L. When in a straight line, the other pins will disappear behind M. Fix another pin N (at least 10 cm from M) such that all four pins appear to be in a straight line.

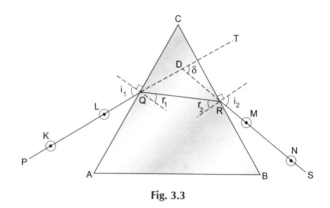

Fig. 3.3

Remove the prism and the pins. Join by a straight line the points where the pins M and N were inserted. This line, SR, meets BC at R. Join Q and R by a straight line. The lines PQ, QR and RS represent the directions of the incident ray, the ray within the prism and the emergent ray respectively.

Draw perpendiculars to AC and BC at Q and R respectively. Measure the angles i_1, r_1, i_2 and r_2. Also, measure the angle of deviation, i.e., the angle between PQ and RS.

Dispersion of Light by a Prism

As with any transparent material, lights of different colours travel at different speeds in the material of a prism. Hence, the refractive index of the material of a prism is different for different colours of light. So, when white light enters a prism, its different components (lights of different colours) bend by different amounts. This causes the components to separate out, or split. While emerging from the prism, they undergo a second refraction and bend further, increasing the separation between the colours. In this way, white light gets split into its component colours on passing through a prism.

Note that the component colours of white light bend by different amounts for all refractions. So, why does not light get split while passing through a rectangular slab? Light bends by equal angles but in opposite directions at the parallel faces of a rectangular slab. So, the components of light that split at the first refraction bend back and recombine to give white light after the second refraction.

Make a narrow slit on a stiff piece of paper and make it stand vertically. Allow sunlight or torchlight to fall on the slit, to create a narrow beam of light. Let this beam fall on a rectangular face of a prism placed near a wall. Light will pass through the prism and fall on the wall. Rotate the prism till you see a band of colours on the wall.

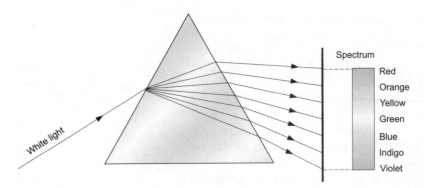

Fig. 3.4 Dispersion of light by a prism produces a spectrum of its component colours. The splitting is exaggerated for clarity.

The band of colours obtained in this activity is continuous, with a colour changing to the next colour in a smooth, gradual way. In other words, there is no sharp boundary between one colour and the next. However, in this band of colours one can distinguish seven main, or prominent, colours. These are violet, indigo, blue, green, yellow, orange and red, in sequence. This sequence of colours can be remembered as VIBGYOR, which is formed by the first letters of the names of the colours. Whenever white light is split, its coloured components appear in this sequence. You see these colours in a rainbow too. When white light is dispersed, violet light deviates the most and red light deviates the least. This means, the refractive index of the prism material is the largest for violet and the least for red. The band of different colours obtained when white light is split is an example of a spectrum, which can be defined as follows.

   The collection of coloured components produced by splitting light is called spectrum.

   In the activity described above, white light is dispersed into its coloured components. We can recombine these components to produce white light. For this, take two similar prisms and keep the second one inverted with respect to the first (Figure 3.5). Let a narrow beam of white light fall on the combination of the prisms, and let the emergent light fall on a wall. You will get a white patch on the wall.

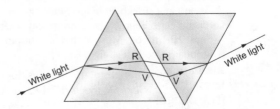

Fig. 3.5 The components of light separated out by a prism can be recombined by passing them through a prism kept inverted with respect to the first.

   The first prism splits white light into its coloured components. When these separated components pass through the second prism, they recombine to form white light. The second prism was kept inverted with respect to the first to recombine the components of white light.

Colour and the Wavelength of Light

The colour of light is related to its wavelength. Table 3.1 gives the relation between the wavelength and colour of light. In the table, the wavelengths are given in nanometres (1 nanometre = 1 nm = 10^{-9} m). Note that among visible lights, red has the longest wavelength, while violet has the shortest.

Table 3.1 Colours and wavelengths of lights

Colour	Wavelength in nm	Colour	Wavelength in nm
Violet	400–440	Yellow	570–590
Indigo	440–460	Orange	590–620
Blue	460–500	Red	620–700
Green	500–570		

Rainbows

A rainbow is perhaps the most beautiful optical phenomenon. It appears as a seven-coloured arc in the sky when there are raindrops in the air. It is visible when the sun is low in the sky (early mornings and late afternoons). To see the rainbow, you have to stand with the sun behind your back.

From where does a rainbow get its colours? The colours come from the dispersion of white light by raindrops suspended in the air. Sunlight entering a drop gets refracted and is split into its component colours. The lights of the component colours travel through the drop and fall on its other side. A part of these lights get reflected, and a part goes out. (This is *not* total internal reflection.) The reflected lights again fall on the surface of the drop and get refracted on the way out. The two refractions bend the lights through a large angle, keeping them separate. The lights of different colours emerging from the raindrops create a rainbow, with red at the top and violet at the bottom.

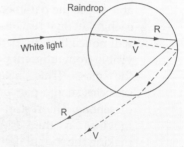

Fig. 3.6 Dispersion by raindrops creates a rainbow.

You can see the rainbow effect at fountains, water sprinklers, waterfalls, and so on. In all these cases, light is dispersed by the droplets of water in the spray. To see the effect, stand with the sun behind you when it is low in the sky.

SCATTERING OF LIGHT

Normally, when you switch on a torch, you do not see a beam of light travelling from the torch. Similarly, during the day you do not see the path of the sunlight as it illuminates things around you. However, you can see the path of light if there is dust, smoke or other small particles in the air. You might have seen the path of sunlight streaming into a room through a gap in the curtains. You might have also seen it coming down through gaps in trees in the early morning mist. In both cases, the path of the light is visible from different positions. You know that light travels in straight lines. So, for us to see the path of light from different positions, light must be redirected in different directions by the particles in its path. The phenomenon in which a part of the light incident on a particle is redirected in different directions is called scattering of light.

When light falls on small particles, a part of it gets scattered in different directions. The rest of the light goes straight through. Do the following activity to see for yourself.

Fig. 3.7 Scattering of light makes its path visible.

Place a glass of tap water in front of a paper screen or wall. Shine a laser pointer (or a small powerful torch) through the water. You will only see spots of light on the screen and on the walls of the glass

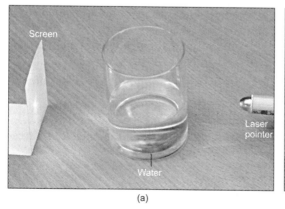

(a)

(b)

Fig. 3.8 The path of light through the water is visible when milk is added to the water.

(Figure 3.8a). Now, put a drop of milk in the water and shine light through the water. You will be able to see the path of the light through the water (Figure 3.8b).

In this activity, the scattering of light by particles of milk in its path enables you to see the path of the light. You are able to see the path because light from each point on it reaches your eyes. You will notice that the path of the light is visible from different positions around the glass. This means that milk particles send a part of the light in all directions. The rest of the light keeps moving in the original direction, making the spot of light on the screen.

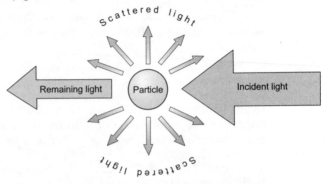

Fig. 3.9 The scattering of light by a particle

A suspension of small particles in a medium is called a colloid. Milk is a colloid in which small fat particles are suspended in water. Smoke is a colloid in which ash particles are suspended in air. Fog and mist are colloids in which droplets of water are suspended in air. You will be able to see the path of a strong beam of light through all of these.

Fig. 3.10 Scattering makes the beams of headlights visible in fog.

The scattering of light by the particles in a colloidal solution is called the Tyndall effect. The scattered light makes the path of light visible. The activity above is also an example of the Tyndall effect.

Scattering of Lights of Different Colours

The colours of light scattered by a suspended particle depends on the size of the particle. Very small particles scatter lights of shorter wavelengths better than those of longer wavelengths. From Table 3.1 it is clear that bluish lights have shorter wavelengths than reddish lights. When white light is incident on small suspended particles, more of the shorter wavelengths of light (bluish lights) get scattered. Very little of longer wavelengths of light (reddish lights) get scattered. So, the remaining light is reddish. The scattering of longer wavelengths of light increases as the size of the particles increases. Large particles scatter lights of all wavelengths equally well.

When smoke contains very fine particles of ash, the bluish lights get scattered, and the smoke looks milky blue. If the particles of ash are large, the entire light incident on it gets scattered. Then the smoke looks white. Clouds look white because of scattering by large drops of water in it.

Take water in a transparent container which is at least 18–20 cm long (or wide). Add two or three drops of milk to the water and shine a powerful torch through the water. Look from a side of the container. You will see that the colour of the milk–water mixture changes with distance from the torch. Near the torch, the colour is milky blue. And at the other end, the colour is orange or red. If you add a few more drops of milk, the colours become darker. Look at the face of the torch through the liquid. It will look reddish.

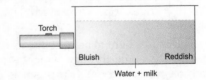

Fig 3.11 The colour of the milk–water mixture changes with distance from the torch.

The suspended particles of milk scatter more of the bluish lights. This makes the mixture look bluish near the torch. As light travels down the container, the components of light left are mainly reddish in colour. So, the light looks orange or red. A similar thing happens in nature to make skies blue and the sun red when it rises or sets.

Colour of the sky

On a clear, sunny day, the sky looks blue. Sunlight travelling through the atmosphere is scattered by the molecules of gases in the air, water droplets, dust particles, and so on. Of these, the smaller ones (like gas molecules) scatter more of the bluish lights. When the scattered light reaches our eyes, it makes the sky look blue.

Air pollution over cities causes large particles to be present in the air above them. Compared to small particles, these particles scatter lights of other colours better. Thus the scattered light has blue as well as some other components. So, the skies over cities look less blue than over open countryside.

In space, there are no particles. So, when astronauts look away from the sun, they only see darkness. This is because there is nothing to scatter sunlight. So, no light gets turned towards their eyes.

Colours of the sun

You must have noticed that the colour of the sun changes during the day. At noon, when the sun is directly overhead, the distance *AB* travelled by sunlight through the atmosphere is short as compared to other times (Figure 3.12). So, sunlight comes across lesser number of particles, resulting in lesser scattering. Thus, around noon, the sun looks close to its actual colour, i.e., white.

At sunset or sunrise, sunlight has to travel a larger distance, *CB*. So, it comes across more number of particles which scatter mostly the bluish lights. Thus, the light reaching our eyes has more of the reddish lights. This makes the sun look orange or red.

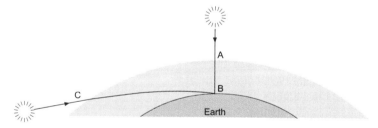

Fig. 3.12 Sunlight travels through a large distance through the atmosphere when the sun is at the horizon.

· POINTS TO REMEMBER ·

- White light is a mixture of coloured lights. The phenomenon of splitting of light into its component colours due to the dependence of refractive index on wavelength is called the *dispersion of light*.

- A prism causes light to be split into its component colours. The angle through which a ray of light turns on passing through a prism is called the *angle of deviation*.

- The collection of coloured components produced by splitting of light is called *spectrum*.

- In dispersion of white light, violet light bends the most and red light bends the least.

- The phenomenon in which a part of the light incident on a particle is redirected in different directions is called *scattering of light*.

- Very small particles scatter lights of shorter wavelengths (bluish lights) better than longer wavelengths. The scattering of longer wavelengths of light (reddish lights) increases as the size of the particles increases. Large particles scatter lights of all wavelengths equally well.

· EXERCISES ·

A. Very-Short-Answer Questions

1. Which is responsible for dispersion of light—reflection or refraction?

2. Define dispersion.

3. Name the component of white light that deviates the least and the component that deviates the most while passing through a glass prism.

4. Name the component of white light that has the longest wavelength.

5. Why do different components of white light deviate through different angles when passing through a prism?

6. Is it necessary that the cross section of a prism be any particular type of triangle such as an equilateral triangle?

7. For which colour—violet or green—does glass have a larger refractive index?

8. What is scattering of light?

B. Short-Answer Questions

1. What is white light? Give a source of white light.

2. After white light passes through a glass prism, its components fall at different positions on a screen. Why?

3. What do you understand by spectrum? How is a spectrum produced in the laboratory?

4. How can you recombine the components of white light after a prism has separated them?

5. What is the relation between the wavelength of light and the size of the particle causing scattering?

6. Why does the sky look blue on a clear, sunny day?

7. Smoke from a fire looks white. What can you deduce about the size of the particles of ash in it?

C. Long-Answer Questions

1. Describe an experiment to show that white light consists of lights of different colours.

2. Describe an experiment to show that certain particles scatter more of some colours of light.

3. Explain why the colour of the sun looks different at different times of the day.

D. Objective Questions

I. *Pick the correct option.*

1. When white light passes through a prism, it splits into its component colours. This phenomenon is called
   (a) spectrum   (b) reflection
   (c) refraction   (d) dispersion

2. The number of surfaces bounding a prism is
   (a) 3   (b) 4   (c) 5   (d) 6

3. A deviation in the path of a ray of light can be produced
   (a) by a glass prism but not by a rectangular glass slab
   (b) by a rectangular glass slab but not by a glass prism
   (c) by a glass prism as well as a rectangular glass slab
   (d) neither by a glass prism nor by a rectangular glass slab

4. The wavelengths corresponding to violet, yellow and red lights are λ_v, λ_y and λ_r respectively.
   (a) $\lambda_v > \lambda_y > \lambda_r$ (b) $\lambda_v < \lambda_y < \lambda_r$
   (c) $\lambda_y < \lambda_v < \lambda_r$ (d) $\lambda_y < \lambda_r < \lambda_v$

5. The sky looks blue on a clear, sunny day because of
   (a) dispersion of light   (b) scattering of light
   (c) reflection of light   (d) refraction of light

II. *Fill in the blanks.*

1. A sodium-vapour lamp emits ...... light.

2. By convention, the angle of incidence for the second refraction in a prism is denoted by ....

3. In a spectrum of white light, the two colours appearing at the ends are ...... and ....

4. The colour in the sequence VIBGYOR that has the least wavelength is ....

5. A small particle will scatter lights of ...... wavelength better.

· ANSWERS ·

D. Objective Questions

I. 1. (d)   **2.** (c)   **3.** (a)   **4.** (b)   **5.** (b)

❖

Electricity

Electricity is indispensable to us. From the humble torch to the powerful computer, thousands of things we use every day need electricity to work. The source of all electricity is charge. As charge is the basis of all electrical phenomena, we often need to know the amount of charge on a body. It is measured in coulombs. The coulomb is the SI unit of charge and its symbol is C.

As you know, matter is generally made of protons, electrons and neutrons. Each proton carries a charge of 1.6×10^{-19} coulomb, and each electron carries an equal negative charge. Neutrons do not carry any net charge. Normally, a body has equal number of protons and electrons, and is therefore, electrically neutral. However, in certain situations, the balance of charges in a body is disturbed. For example, when a glass rod is rubbed with a silk cloth, some electrons get transferred from the glass rod to the silk. The silk cloth, which gains electrons, becomes negatively charged. And the glass rod, which is left with more protons than electrons, becomes positively charged.

Charged particles or objects can exert forces on each other. While like (similar) charges repel each other, unlike charges attract. Another important thing about charged particles is that they can flow, i.e., they can move in a particular direction. This flow of charged particles is called an electric current. Charged particles such as electrons are present in all substances. But, they do not flow on their own. For flow of charges, there has to be a potential difference.

POTENTIAL DIFFERENCE AND THE FLOW OF CHARGE

An electrical potential difference arises out of charges. Consider a group of stationary charges (Figure 4.1). A separate charge q is placed at B. It experiences a force exerted by the group of charges. This affects the force required, and hence, the work done (W) in moving q to the point A. The quantity W/q is called the potential difference between A and B. In other words, the potential difference between two points A and B is the work done per unit charge in taking a charge from B to A. We express this mathematically as

$$V = V_A - V_B = \frac{W}{q}$$

...4.1

Here, V is the potential difference between the points A and B, and V_A and V_B are the potentials at these points.

While defining coordinates of a point in mathematics, you choose a point, call it the origin, and say that its coordinates are (0, 0). The coordinates of all other points are found by measuring the distances from this point. Similarly, you can choose a reference point and say that the potential there is zero. The potentials of other points are found with respect to this point. Quite often, the potential at infinity is chosen as zero.

If B be the reference point, the potential at B is $V_B = 0$. From Equation 4.1, the potential at A is $V_A = W/q$. So, the potential at a point is the work done per unit charge in taking a charge to that point from a chosen reference point. Equation 4.1 may also be written as

$$W = qV. \qquad \qquad ...4.2$$

The work done on the charge q is stored as the electric potential energy (U) of the group of charges. So,

$$U = qV. \qquad \qquad ...4.3$$

Unit of potential difference The unit of potential difference (and potential) is the volt, whose symbol is V. The volt is named in honour of the Italian physicist Alessandro Volta (1745–1827). If 1 joule of work is done in taking 1 coulomb of charge from one point to another, the potential difference between the points is 1 volt.

$$V = \frac{W}{q} = \frac{1 \text{ joule}}{1 \text{ coulomb}} = 1 \text{ volt}.$$

The potential difference between two points is sometimes also called the voltage.

Flow of Charge

Consider two identical metallic spheres P and N, carrying equal amounts of positive and negative charges respectively (Figure 4.2). A positive charge is to be taken from B to A. It is attracted by the negatively charged sphere N and repelled by the positively charged sphere P. So, to move the charge towards A, one has to apply a force on it towards the left. Thus, the work done is positive. Hence, the potential difference $V_A - V_B$ is positive. This means $V_A > V_B$.

As one moves towards P, the work done increases; so, the potential increases. And on moving towards N, the potential decreases. So, the potential of P is higher than that of N. In general, the potential of a positively charged body is taken as higher than that of a negatively charged body.

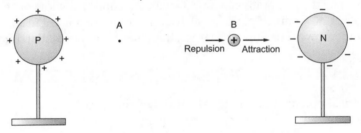

Fig. 4.2

What happens when a free-to-move charge is placed between the spheres? A positive charge will move towards the negatively charged sphere. And a negative charge will move towards the positively charged sphere. That is, a free positive charge moves towards lower potential. And a free negative charge moves towards higher potential.

If the two spheres are connected by a metal wire, electrons from the negatively charged sphere (at a lower potential) will flow to the positively charged sphere (at a higher potential). Eventually, the flow of electrons causes the charges on the spheres to become balanced. When that happens, the spheres no longer carry a net charge, and therefore, have equal potential. So, the flow of electrons stops. We can thus say that a potential difference causes charges to flow.

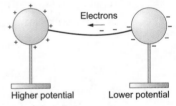

Fig. 4.3

A Cell Provides a Constant Potential Difference

The potential difference provided by things like charged spheres reduces to zero quickly once charges start to flow. So, we have to use cells to provide constant potential difference for a long time. Cells have chemicals inside. Reactions in the cell cause positive and negative charges to gather separately. This creates a potential difference between the terminals of the cell. The terminal at a higher potential is called the positive terminal and the one at a lower potential is called the negative terminal.

The cells that we commonly use are called dry cells (Figure 4.4a). In a common dry cell, the small metallic cap at one end is the positive terminal, while the flat metallic plate at the other end is the negative terminal. It provides a potential difference of 1.5 V. A cell is represented by the symbol shown in Figure 4.4b. The larger line represents the positive terminal, while the shorter line represents the negative terminal.

A combination of cells is called a battery. Quite often, multiple cells are combined to get a potential difference that is higher than that of a single cell. For example, we connect two 1.5-V cells to get a potential difference of 3 V (Figure 4.4c). This is shown using symbols in Figure 4.4d.

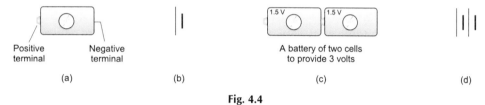

| Positive terminal | Negative terminal | | A battery of two cells to provide 3 volts | |
| (a) | (b) | | (c) | (d) |

Fig. 4.4

ELECTRIC CURRENT

Consider a metallic wire ACB connected across a cell of potential difference V. Since the end A is connected to the positive terminal, it is at a higher potential than the end B. In metals, some electrons are loosely bound to the atoms, and can move within it. These are called free electrons. In the metallic wire, these electrons (negative charges) move from the low-potential side B to the high-potential side A. After reaching A, they enter the cell. The chemical reactions in the cell drive these electrons to the negative terminal. From there, they re-enter the wire at the end B. Thus, there is a continuous flow of electrons in the wire from B to C to A. We say that there is an electric current in the wire.

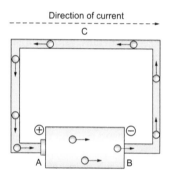

Fig. 4.5 Current in a wire connected to a cell

In a metal, the flow of negative charges constitutes the current. An electric current can also be a flow of positive charges. So, a flow of charge is called an electric current.

By convention, the direction of current is taken as the direction of flow of positive charges. Thus, the direction of current is opposite to the direction of flow of negative charges. So, when a wire is connected to a cell, the current in the wire is from the positive-terminal end to the negative-terminal end.

Measurement of Current

The charge passing per unit time through a given place is the magnitude of the electric current at that place. Thus,

$$i = \frac{Q}{t}$$

...**4.4**

Here Q is the charge that passes through a place in time t.

Unit of current From Equation 4.4, we find that current is charge divided by time. The SI unit of charge is the coulomb and that of time is the second. The SI unit of current, therefore, is coulomb/second. This unit is called the ampere, whose symbol is A. Thus, if one coulomb of charge passes through a place in one second, the current there is 1 ampere. The ampere is named in honour of the French physicist André Marie Ampère (1775–1836), who made many contributions that helped our understanding of electricity.

EXAMPLE 4.1 6×10^{17} **electrons cross through an area per minute. What is the electric current?**

Solution   The charge carried by an electron $= 1.6 \times 10^{-19}$C.

Total charge carried by 6×10^{17} electrons is $Q = 6 \times 10^{17} \times 1.6 \times 10^{-19}$C.

So, the current $i = \dfrac{Q}{t} = \dfrac{6 \times 10^{17} \times 1.6 \times 10^{-19} \ \text{C}}{60 \ \text{s}} = 1.6 \times 10^{-3}\text{A} = 1.6 \ \text{mA}.$

Conductors and Insulators

Materials that conduct electricity easily are called good conductors or simply, conductors. And, materials that do not conduct electricity easily are called insulators.

All metals conduct electricity because they have some loosely bound free electrons, which flow when a potential difference is applied. However, some metals conduct electricity better than others. Silver is the best conductor. But because of the high cost of silver, electric wires are made of copper, or in some cases aluminium.

Most nonmetallic solids do not conduct electricity. Although diamond and graphite are both forms of carbon (a nonmetal), graphite is a conductor while diamond is an insulator. Insulators do not conduct electricity because their electrons are tightly bound to the atoms. Rubber, plastics, wood, glass and porcelain are some examples of insulators. Insulators have many uses. For example, they are used as protective covers on electric wires and electrician's tools.

Certain liquids also conduct electricity. While distilled water is an insulator, addition of certain salts, acids or bases allows it to conduct electricity. Under normal circumstances, gases do not conduct electricity.

ELECTRIC CIRCUITS AND MEASURING INSTRUMENTS

A closed path in which a current can flow is called an electric circuit. An electric circuit may have one or more electric elements such as bulbs (or lamps), cells, switches (or plug keys), metal wires, etc. Each element of a circuit has a specific function to play. For example, wires can be used to connect one element to the next. And a plug key or a switch can be used to either complete or break the closed path, thereby starting or stopping the current in the circuit.

Figure 4.6a shows a simple electric circuit in which a bulb, a cell and a plug key are connected by wires. With the key out of the plug, no current flows through the circuit. In Figure 4.6b, the key is in the plug, completing the circuit. In experiments, the plug key or switch should be closed only when required, like when making measurements. This prevents the cell or battery from draining out quickly.

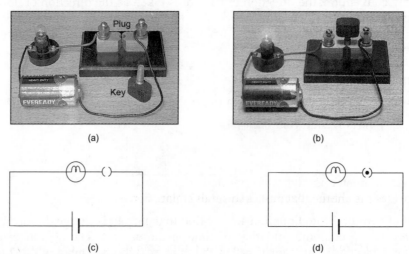

(a)   (b)

(c)   (d)

Fig. 4.6 Circuits and circuit diagrams

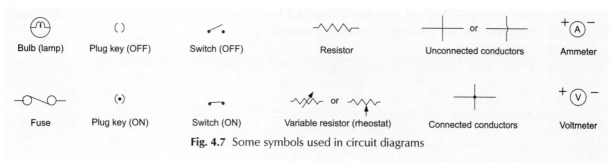

Fig. 4.7 Some symbols used in circuit diagrams

A circuit may be represented by a diagram that uses symbols for the elements used in the circuit, showing how the elements are connected to each other. Such a diagram is called a circuit diagram. In Figure 4.6, parts c and d are the circuit diagrams for the open and closed circuits shown in parts a and b of the figure. The bulb, cell and the plug key are represented by their symbols. Some common circuit elements and their symbols are shown in Figure 4.7.

Common Measuring Instruments

The electric current in a circuit is measured by an instrument called the ammeter, and the potential difference between two points in it is measured by a voltmeter. You might have seen these meters in voltage stabilizers. In these meters, a needle moving over a graduated scale gives the value of the measured quantity. Each meter has two terminals. The terminal marked '+' is connected by a wire to the higher-potential side of a circuit, while the terminal marked '–' is connected to the lower-potential side.

(a)

(b)

Fig. 4.8 (a) Ammeter (b) Voltmeter

Using an ammeter to measure current

To measure the current through an element of a circuit, an ammeter is connected in such a way that the current flowing through it also flows through the element. Such a connection is called a series connection. In Figure 4.9, the current i flowing through the lamp also flows through the ammeter. The reading of the ammeter gives the current through the lamp. Note that if the ammeter is removed, there will be a gap, and the current through the circuit will stop.

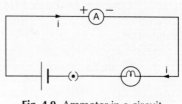

Fig. 4.9 Ammeter in a circuit

Two or more electric elements are said to be connected in series if the current flowing through one also flows through the rest.

An ammeter is always connected in series in a circuit. The connection of the cells in Figure 4.4c is another example of a series connection.

Using a voltmeter to measure potential difference

Figure 4.10 shows a circuit that has two lamps connected to a cell. Suppose we want to measure the potential difference across the lamp L_2, i.e., between the points A and B. As A is on the side of the positive terminal of the cell, its potential is higher than that of B. So, the '+' terminal of the voltmeter is connected to A, and the '−' terminal, to B. The reading of the voltmeter gives the potential difference across L_2.

Here, the current flowing through the voltmeter is different from those flowing through the other elements of the circuit. Also, even if the voltmeter is removed, the current continues to flow in the circuit. Note that the potential difference across L_2 and the voltmeter is the same. Such a connection is called a parallel connection.

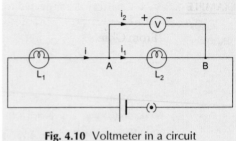

Fig. 4.10 Voltmeter in a circuit

Two or more electric elements are said to be connected in parallel if the same potential difference exists across them.

OHM'S LAW

When a torch is used for several weeks, its light becomes dim. We say that its cells have become weak. What does it mean? It means that the potential differences across the terminals of the cells have reduced. When you buy a new 1.5-volt dry cell, the potential difference across its terminals is 1.5 V. When the cell is used for a long time, the potential difference drops to a smaller value, say, 0.75 V. When such a cell is used in a torch, less current flows through the bulb, and hence, it produces less light. So, we see that the electric current passing through an element depends on the potential difference applied across it. The larger is the potential difference, the larger is the current. This relationship between potential difference and current was first established by the German physicist Georg Simon Ohm (1787–1854) and is stated by the law named after him.

Ohm's Law	*The current through a metallic element is proportional to the potential difference applied between its ends, provided the temperature remains constant.*

If a potential difference V is applied to an element and a current i passes through it,

$$i \propto V$$

or

$$i = \left(\frac{1}{R}\right)V. \qquad \qquad \text{...4.5}$$

Thus,

Ohm's Law	$V = iR$

...4.6

Here R is a constant for the given element and is called its resistance.

Resistance

From Equation 4.5, $\qquad \qquad i = \dfrac{V}{R}.$

So, for a given potential difference, $\qquad i \propto \dfrac{1}{R}.$

Thus, for a given potential difference, the current is inversely proportional to the resistance. The higher is the resistance, the lower is the current. If the resistance is doubled, the current is halved. Good conductors have low resistance, while insulators have very high resistance.

Unit of resistance Potential difference is measured in volts, and current is measured in amperes. From Equation 4.6, $R = V/i$. So, the unit of resistance is volt/ampere. This unit is called the ohm, and its symbol is Ω. We can define one ohm as follows.

If a potential difference of 1 volt is applied across an element, and a current of 1 ampere passes through it, the resistance of the element is called 1 ohm.

EXAMPLE 4.2 A 4-V battery is connected to a lamp of resistance 4 Ω. Calculate the current through the lamp.

Solution   From Ohm's law, $i = \dfrac{V}{R} = \dfrac{4\,V}{4\,\Omega} = 1$ A.

Verification of Ohm's Law

Take four or five dry cells, a thin wire (*AB*), a voltmeter, an ammeter, a plug key and some thick connecting wires. Connect the circuit as shown in Figure 4.11a, using one cell. The plug key allows you to switch off the current when not required. The wire becomes quite hot when current passes through it for some time. This drains the cell as well. Therefore, insert the key into the plug to switch on the current only when taking measurements.

The ammeter measures the current *i* through the circuit, and the voltmeter measures the potential difference *V* between the ends *A* and *B* of the wire. Note these values. Now connect two cells in series in the circuit, as shown in Figure 4.11b. You will find that the reading of the voltmeter increases, indicating the fact that a larger potential difference has been applied across the wire *AB*. You will also find that the reading of the ammeter increases as well. Note down the new values of *V* and *i*. Repeat the experiment by connecting in series three cells, four cells, and so on. In each case measure the potential difference and the current. If you calculate *V/i* for each, you will find that it is almost the same. So, *V/i = R* is a constant, which is another way of stating Ohm's law. Here, *R* is the resistance of the wire *AB*. If you plot a graph of the current *i* against the potential difference *V*, it will be a straight line (Figure 4.11c). This shows that the current is proportional to the potential difference.

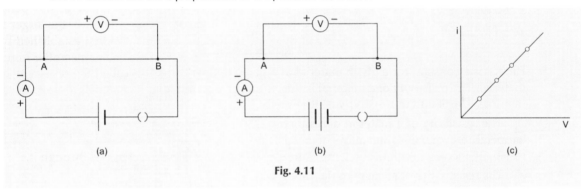

(a)   (b)   (c)

Fig. 4.11

On What Does Resistance Depend?

Resistance depends on the material We have seen that for a given wire, the current is proportional to the potential difference applied across it. What if we take a wire of a different material? Connect a circuit as shown in Figure 4.12, in which *AB* represents a wire. Take wires of different materials, but of the same cross-sectional area (same thickness) and the same length. You may take a Nichrome wire, fuse wire, copper wire, an iron wire, and so on. Connect each wire one by one between *A* and *B*. After connecting a particular wire, insert the key into the plug. Then read the ammeter to note the current (*i*) passing through that wire. You will find that the value of the current is different for different wires. Since the same cell is used every time, the potential difference (*V*) across the wires is the same. You can of course verify this by connecting a voltmeter across *AB*.

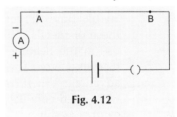

The different wires used in this experiment drew different currents when the same potential difference was applied across them. This means, the resistance of a wire of given length and cross-sectional area depends on the material of the wire.

Fig. 4.12

Resistance depends on area of cross section Repeat the above experiment with wires of the same material and the same length, but of different cross-sectional areas. You will find that the thicker the wire, the greater the current. So, the thicker wires have lesser resistance than the thinner wires. In fact, resistance is inversely proportional to the area of cross section (*A*).

$$R \propto \frac{1}{A}.$$ ...(i)

Now, you know why we use thick wires for connecting different elements of a circuit. It ensures that their resistance is negligible.

Resistance depends on length Take wires of the same material and the same thickness, but of different lengths. If the length of the first wire is, say, l, the other wires should be of length $2l$, $3l$, and so on. Find the resistance (V/i) of the first wire and then compare it with that of the others. You will find that when the length is doubled, the current is halved. In other words, the resistance is doubled. And, when the length becomes three times, the resistance also increases three times. Thus, resistance is proportional to length.

$$R \propto l.$$ ...(ii)

Resistance depends on temperature Apart from these, resistance depends slightly on temperature. In general, resistance increases with increase in temperature.

Resistivity

We found that for a given material, resistance is (i) inversely proportional to the area of cross section, and (ii) directly proportional to length. Combining (i) and (ii),

$$R \propto \frac{l}{A}$$

or

$$\boxed{R = \rho \frac{l}{A}}$$ ...4.7

Here, ρ is a constant for a given material at a given temperature. It is called the resistivity of the material. The resistivity of a material is the resistance per unit length of a unit cross section of the material. The SI unit of resistivity is ohm metre.

The resistivity of a material depends on its temperature. For metals and alloys of metals, the resistivity increases with rise in temperature.

The resistivities of some materials are given in Table 4.1. Note that the values of resistivity of metals are very small—of the order of $10^{-8} \Omega$ m. This makes them good conductors. Metals such as copper are therefore used for making electric wires. The filament of an electric bulb (incandescent lamp) is usually made of tungsten, as the melting point of tungsten is very high.

The values of resistivity of insulators such as glass and fused quartz are very high—of the order of $10^{16} \Omega$ m. Alloys like Nichrome have 30–100 times larger values of resistivity than those of metals. This makes them suitable for use in the heating elements of electric irons, toasters, etc. These alloys also have an advantage—their resistance varies very little with temperature, and these do not oxidize readily.

The resistivities of materials such as silicon and germanium are $10^5 – 10^{10}$ times more than that of metals, but $10^{15} – 10^{16}$ times less than that of insulators like fused quartz. Such materials are called semiconductors. Semiconductors are

Table 4.1　Resistivities at 20°C

Material	Resistivity (Ω m)
Metals	
Silver	1.6×10^{-8}
Copper	1.7×10^{-8}
Aluminium	2.8×10^{-8}
Tungsten	5.8×10^{-8}
Iron	9.7×10^{-8}
Alloys	
Manganin	48.2×10^{-8}
Nichrome	100×10^{-8}
Semiconductors	
Germanium	4.7×10^{-3}
Silicon	2.5×10^{3}
Insulators	
Diamond	5×10^{12}
Fused quartz	$10^{16} – 10^{19}$

Fig. 4.13 An integrated circuit

used to make integrated circuits (ICs). ICs are used in all sorts of electronic devices, including computers, TVs, modern telephones, etc.

SERIES AND PARALLEL CONNECTIONS OF RESISTORS

A conducting material (e.g., a wire) of a particular resistance meant for use in a circuit is called a resistor. A resistor is sometimes simply referred to as a resistance. It is represented by the symbol ─∿∿─ . Two or more resistors can be connected in series, in parallel or in a manner that is a combination of these two.

Series Connection of Resistors

Two or more resistors are said to be connected in series if the current flowing through one also flows through the rest.

1. You can use different kinds of bulbs as resistors in this activity. Connect three resistors of resistances R_1, R_2 and R_3 to an ammeter, a cell and a plug key, as shown in Figure 4.14a. The three resistors are connected in series. Close the key and note the ammeter reading. Now connect the ammeter between R_1 and R_2 (Figure 4.14b) and note the reading. Similarly, place the ammeter between the other circuit elements and measure the current. You will find that the value of the current is the same everywhere in the circuit. So, the same current passes through the three resistors.

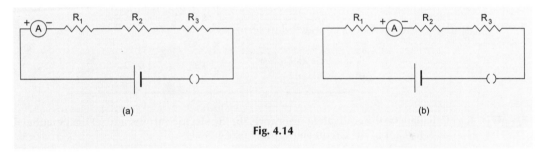

(a)   (b)

Fig. 4.14

2. Now, connect a voltmeter in the circuit, as shown in Figure 4.15a. Close the key and note the potential difference V across the series combination of resistors. Then connect the voltmeter across R_1 (Figure 4.15b) and note the reading V_1. Similarly, connect the voltmeter across R_2 and R_3 one at a time, and measure the potential differences V_2 and V_3 across them.

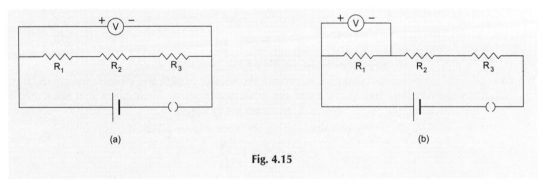

(a)   (b)

Fig. 4.15

You will find that

$$V = V_1 + V_2 + V_3.$$

So, the potential difference across the combination of resistors connected in series is equal to the sum of the potential differences across the individual resistors.

Equivalent resistance in series connection

Figure 4.16a shows three resistors of resistances R_1, R_2 and R_3 connected in series. The cell connected across the combination maintains a potential difference V across the combination. The current through the cell is i. The same current i flows through each resistor.

Let us replace the combination of resistors by a single resistor R_{eq} such that the current does not change, i.e., it remains i (Figure 4.16b). This resistance is called the equivalent resistance of the combination, and its value is given by Ohm's law as $R_{eq} = V/i$.

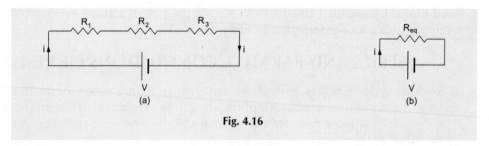

Fig. 4.16

Thus, $$V = iR_{eq}.$$

The potential differences V_1, V_2 and V_3 across the resistors R_1, R_2 and R_3 respectively are given by Ohm's law as

$$V_1 = iR_1 \qquad V_2 = iR_2 \qquad V_3 = iR_3$$

Since the resistors are in series,

$$V = V_1 + V_2 + V_3.$$

Substituting the values of the potential differences in the above equation,

$$iR_{eq} = iR_1 + iR_2 + iR_3$$

or $$iR_{eq} = i(R_1 + R_2 + R_3)$$

or $$R_{eq} = R_1 + R_2 + R_3.$$

Similarly, for n resistors connected in series,

Equivalent Resistance of Resistors in Series	$R_{eq} = R_1 + R_2 + R_3 + ... + R_n$	...4.8

EXAMPLE 4.3 Calculate (a) the equivalent resistance, (b) the electric current, and (c) the potential difference across each resistor in the circuit shown in Figure 4.17a.

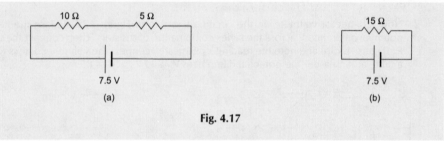

Fig. 4.17

Solution

(a) Any current that passes through the resistor of $10\,\Omega$ also passes through the resistor of $5\,\Omega$. So, the 10-Ω and 5-Ω resistors are connected in series. Their equivalent resistance is

$$R = 10\,\Omega + 5\,\Omega = 15\,\Omega.$$

(b) The circuit is equivalent to that shown in Figure 4.17b. The current is

$$i = \frac{V}{R} = \frac{7.5\,V}{15\,\Omega} = 0.5\ A.$$

This is the current through both the resistors.

(c) The potential difference across the 10-Ω resistor is

$$V_1 = iR_1 = (0.5\ A) \times (10\,\Omega) = 5\ V.$$

The potential difference across the 5-Ω resistor is

$$V_2 = iR_2 = (0.5\ A) \times (5\,\Omega) = 2.5\ V.$$

Parallel Connection of Resistors

Connect three resistors (R_1, R_2 and R_3), an ammeter, a cell and a plug key, as shown in Figure 4.18a. Close the key and note the ammeter reading. This gives the current i in the circuit. Now, connect the ammeter in the branch of the circuit that has R_1 (Figure 4.18b) and note the reading. This gives the current i_1 through the branch. Similarly, place the ammeter in the branches containing R_2 and R_3, and measure the currents i_2 and i_3 respectively.

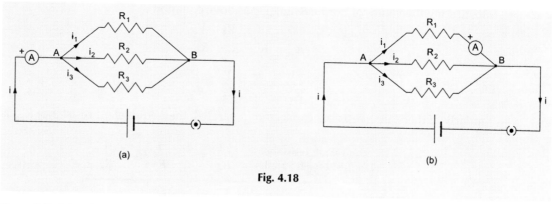

Fig. 4.18

You will find that the current i gets divided into the branches such that

$$i = i_1 + i_2 + i_3.$$

So, the total current flowing into the combination is equal to the sum of the currents passing through the individual resistors.

Note that in the activity all the resistors are connected between the common points A and B. The potential difference between the points is $V_A - V_B$. This potential difference exists across each resistor.

If resistors are connected in such a way that the same potential difference gets applied to each of them, they are said to be connected in parallel.

Equivalent resistance in parallel connection

Figure 4.19a shows three resistors of resistances R_1, R_2 and R_3 connected in parallel across the points A and B. The cell connected across these two points maintains a potential difference V across each resistor. The current through the cell is i. It gets divided at A into three parts i_1, i_2 and i_3, which flow through R_1, R_2 and R_3 respectively.

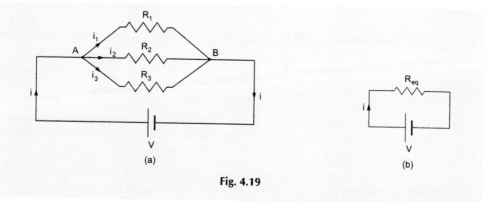

Fig. 4.19

Let us replace the combination of resistors by an equivalent resistor R_{eq} such that the current i in the circuit does not change (Figure 4.19a). The equivalent resistance is given by Ohm's law as $R_{eq} = V/i$. Thus,

$$i = \frac{V}{R_{eq}}.$$

The currents i_1, i_2 and i_3 through the resistors R_1, R_2 and R_3 respectively are given by Ohm's law as

$$i_1 = \frac{V}{R_1} \qquad i_2 = \frac{V}{R_2} \qquad i_3 = \frac{V}{R_3}$$

Since the resistors are in parallel,

$$i = i_1 + i_2 + i_3.$$

Substituting the values of the currents in the above equation,

$$\frac{V}{R_{eq}} = \frac{V}{R_1} + \frac{V}{R_2} + \frac{V}{R_3}$$

or

$$\frac{1}{R_{eq}} = \frac{1}{R_1} + \frac{1}{R_2} + \frac{1}{R_3}.$$

Similarly, if there are n resistors connected in parallel, their equivalent resistance R_{eq} is given by

| Equivalent Resistance of Resistors in Parallel | $\dfrac{1}{R_{eq}} = \dfrac{1}{R_1} + \dfrac{1}{R_2} + \ldots + \dfrac{1}{R_n}$ | ...4.9 |

For two resistances R_1 and R_2 connected in parallel,

$$\frac{1}{R} = \frac{1}{R_1} + \frac{1}{R_2} = \frac{R_1 + R_2}{R_1 R_2}$$

or

$$R = \frac{R_1 R_2}{R_1 + R_2} \qquad \ldots 4.10$$

We see that the equivalent resistance in a parallel connection is less than each of the resistances.

You can use this result to explain why the resistance of a metallic wire is inversely proportional to its area of cross section. You can think of a thick wire as a parallel combination of several thin wires. The resistance of the combination is less than that of each of the thin wires. In other words, the resistance of a thick wire is less than that of a thin wire.

EXAMPLE 4.4 **Two resistances of 3 Ω and 6 Ω are connected in parallel. Calculate their equivalent resistance.**

Solution   The equivalent resistance is

$$R = \frac{R_1 R_2}{R_1 + R_2} = \frac{(3\,\Omega) \times (6\,\Omega)}{(3\,\Omega) + (6\,\Omega)} = \frac{18\,\Omega^2}{9\,\Omega} = 2\,\Omega.$$

EXAMPLE 4.5 **A 1-Ω resistor is connected in parallel to a 10-Ω resistor. Calculate the equivalent resistance.**

Solution   The equivalent resistance is

$$R = \frac{R_1 R_2}{R_1 + R_2} = \frac{(1\,\Omega) \times (100\,\Omega)}{(1\,\Omega) + (100\,\Omega)} = \frac{100}{101}\,\Omega = 0.99\,\Omega.$$

We find that when a resistance is joined parallel to a comparatively smaller resistance, the equivalent resistance is very close to the value of the smaller resistance.

Note that if a resistor connected in series with others is removed or fails, the current through each resistor becomes zero. On the other hand, if a resistor connected in parallel with others fails or is removed, the current continues to flow through the other resistors.

Distribution of Current in Two Resistors in Parallel

Consider the circuit in Figure 4.20. The resistors R_1 and R_2 are connected in parallel. The current i gets distributed in the two resistors.

We have $i = i_1 + i_2$.   (i)

Applying Ohm's law to the resistor R_1,

$$V_A - V_B = R_1 i_1. \qquad (ii)$$

And applying Ohm's law to the resistor R_2,

$$V_A - V_B = R_2 i_2. \qquad (iii)$$

From (ii) and (iii), $R_1 i_1 = R_2 i_2$ or $i_2 = \dfrac{R_1}{R_2} i_1.$

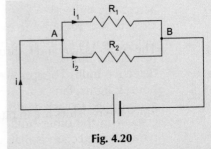

Fig. 4.20

Substituting for i_2 in (i), we have

$$i = i_1 + \frac{R_1}{R_2} i_1 = i_1\left(1 + \frac{R_1}{R_2}\right) = i_1 \frac{R_1 + R_2}{R_2}$$

or

$$i_1 = \frac{R_2}{R_1 + R_2} i \qquad \qquad ...4.11$$

Similarly,

$$i_2 = \frac{R_1}{R_1 + R_2} i \qquad \qquad ...4.12$$

Thus,

$$\frac{i_1}{i_2} = \frac{R_2}{R_1}.$$

The current through each branch in a parallel combination of resistors is inversely proportional to its resistance.

EXAMPLE 4.6 Two resistors of resistances $10\,\Omega$ and $20\,\Omega$ are connected in parallel. A battery supplies 6 A of current to the combination, as shown in Figure 4.21. Calculate the current in each resistor.

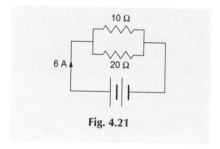

Fig. 4.21

Solution The current in the 10-Ω resistor is

$$i_1 = \frac{R_2}{R_1 + R_2} i = \frac{(20\,\Omega) \times (6\text{ A})}{(10\,\Omega) + (20\,\Omega)} = 4\text{ A}.$$

The current in the 20-Ω resistor is

$$i_2 = \frac{R_1}{R_1 + R_2} i = \frac{(10\,\Omega) \times (6\text{ A})}{(10\,\Omega) + (20\,\Omega)} = 2\text{ A}.$$

Devices in Series and Parallel

You must have seen tiny bulbs strung together for decorating buildings during festivals like Diwali, and occasions like marriages, etc. These bulbs are connected in series, and the mains voltage is applied to the combination. The potential difference (V) of the mains gets divided across the bulbs ($V = V_1 + V_2 + V_3 + ...$). So, a small potential difference exists across each bulb, close to that required to make the bulb work. However, the same current flows through all the bulbs. So, if one bulb goes bad, the current through it stops, and this stops the current through the rest of the bulbs as well. To make the chain of lights work, you have to find and replace the defective bulb. This problem does not occur with the lights in your house. That is because in houses, lights, fans, etc., are connected in parallel. In parallel connection, the same mains voltage gets applied to each device, but the current through each is different. If one of them goes bad, the current in the other branches of the parallel connection does not stop. Another advantage of parallel connection is that, unlike series connection, each device can draw a different current, as per its requirement.

Fig. 4.22 Bulbs connected in series are used for decoration.

HEATING EFFECT OF ELECTRIC CURRENT

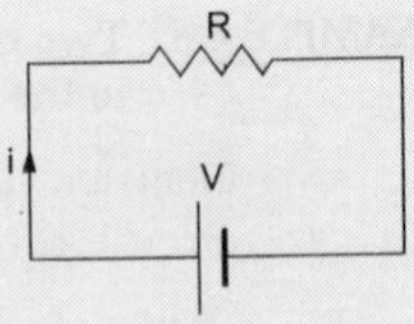

When an electric current passes through a bulb, the filament gets so hot that it glows and emits light. When a current passes through the filament of an electric iron, the iron becomes very hot. This increase in temperature is due to what is called 'the heat produced due to current'.

Fig. 4.23

Suppose a resistor R is connected to a cell (Figure 4.23). The cell maintains a potential difference V across the resistor, driving a current i through it. So,

$$V = iR. \tag{i}$$

The current through the resistor is actually a flow of negative charges (electrons). Inside the cell, the negative charges flow from the positive to the negative terminal. The cell does work $= QV$ to take a charge through the potential difference V between its terminals. This increases the energy of the charge by QV. This increased energy gets converted to heat in the resistor. So, the energy appearing as heat is given by

$$U = QV. \tag{ii}$$

The charge that passes through the wire in time t is

$$Q = it. \tag{iii}$$

Using (i), (ii) and (iii), we find that the heat produced in the wire in time t is

$$U = QV = (it)(iR) = i^2Rt.$$

Heat Produced by Current	$U = i^2Rt$

...**4.13**

From Equation 4.13 we see that the heat produced is proportional to the square of the current, if R and t remain constant. So, if the current passing for a given time through a given resistance is doubled, the heat produced becomes four times. Similarly, for a given i and t, the heat produced is proportional to R. If the same current i passes through two resistances in a given time, more heat will be produced in the larger resistance.

The heat produced can also be written as

$$U = i^2Rt = \left(\frac{V}{R}\right)^2 Rt$$

or

$$U = \frac{V^2}{R}t$$

...**4.14**

For a given V and t, the heat produced is inversely proportional to R. So, if the same potential difference is applied across two resistances, more heat will be produced in the smaller resistance.

EXAMPLE 4.7 A 3-V battery is connected across a 5-Ω resistance. Calculate the heat produced in 5 seconds.

Solution   The heat produced is $U = \dfrac{V^2}{R} t = \dfrac{(3\text{ V})^2}{5\ \Omega} \times 5\text{ s} = 9\text{ J}.$

We have seen above that the increased energy of a charge gets converted to heat in the resistor. The increase in energy comes from the work done by the cell. This uses up the chemical energy of the cell. So, the energy appearing as heat in the resistor ultimately comes at the expense of the chemical energy of the cell.

Not always is the work done by a cell converted to heat. Immediately after a motor is connected to a cell, the speed of the shaft of the motor increases. A part of the work done by the cell goes into producing the increase in kinetic energy. And a part is used to overcome friction, etc. When the motor achieves a constant speed, its kinetic energy does not change. So the work done by the cell is only used to overcome friction, etc. This appears as heat. That is why the cover over a motor becomes warm on use.

Electric Power

Power is the rate of doing work, or the rate at which energy is produced or consumed. The electrical energy produced or consumed per unit time is called electric power. In an electric circuit, the power is

$$P = \frac{U}{t} = \frac{i^2 R t}{t} = i^2 R.$$

Electric Power	$P = i^2 R$	...4.15

Using $iR = V$,

$P = Vi$	...4.16

$P = \dfrac{V^2}{R}$	...4.17

The energy consumed and power are related as

$U = Pt$	...4.18

Unit of Power The SI unit of energy is the joule, and that of time is the second. The SI unit of power is therefore joule/second. This unit is called the watt, whose symbol is W. It is named in honour of the British inventor James Watt (1736–1819), famous for his steam engine.

Applications of the Heating Effect of Current

The heating effect of electric current has many uses. Electric bulbs, room heaters, electric irons, immersion heaters, toasters, electric fuses and a number of other appliances work on this principle. In all of these, a wire of suitable resistance, commonly called the *heating element*, is connected to the power supply. The current passing through the element produces heat in it, which is used for some specific purpose. We shall discuss two common devices here.

Electric bulb

An electric bulb has a simple structure. It consists of a sealed glass bulb that has a tungsten filament connected to two electrical contacts. The bulb is filled with an unreactive gas like argon or nitrogen. To produce white light, the filament has to be heated to about 3000°C by passing a current through it. Obviously, the material of the filament should such that it does not melt at this temperature. Tungsten is used for the filament because its melting point is about 3400°C. The sealed glass bulb serves two purposes. First, it protects the filament from oxidation and the effects of humidity. Secondly, the small enclosed volume makes it easier to maintain the required temperature, as without it the loss of heat would be more.

Fig. 4.24 Electric bulb

Fuse

A fuse is a safety device that does not allow excessive current to flow through an electric circuit. It consists of a metallic wire of low melting point, fixed between the two terminals of a fuse plug. The fuse plug fits into a fuse socket connected in the circuit. Fuses are available in various shapes. Figure 4.25 shows common types of fuses. The fuse plug shown in Figure 4.25a is used in household wiring. It is made of porcelain. The fuse plug shown in Figure 4.25b is used in electric appliances such as TVs, invertors, amplifiers, etc.

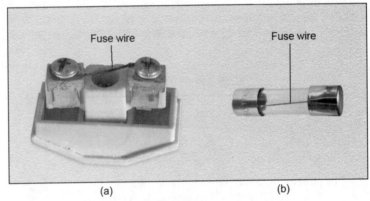

(a)   (b)

Fig. 4.25

A fuse is connected in series with an appliance (such as a TV) or a group of appliances (such as the lights and fans in a room). So, the current through the fuse is the same as the current through the appliance or the group of appliances. If this current exceeds a safe value, the heat produced in the fuse wire causes it to melt immediately. This breaks the circuit, preventing any damage. Figure 4.26 shows examples of how a fuse is connected in circuits.

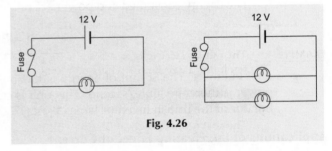

Fig. 4.26

Good-quality fuse wires are made of tin, as it has a low melting point. Some fuse wires are made of an alloy of tin and copper. The thickness of the fuse wire depends on the circuit in which it is to be used. If a section of the circuit is meant to carry a maximum of 5 A current, the fuse wire should also be able to carry currents up to 5 A. Similarly, for wiring meant for 15 A, the fuse wire should be thicker, and should be able to carry currents up to 15 A.

Disadvantages of the Heating Effect of Current

A current always produces some heat, whether we use the heat or not. If the heat produced cannot be utilized, it represents a wastage of energy. A considerable amount of energy is thus wasted in the transmission of electricity from the generating station to our homes. Sometimes, the heat produced in a device is so much that it can damage the device, unless proper cooling arrangements are made. To dissipate the heat produced in TV sets, monitors, etc., their cabinets have grills for air to pass. Certain components of a computer get so hot that they have fans to cool them.

Rating of Electric Appliances

Take an electric bulb and see what is written on it. Apart from the name and the symbol of the company, you will find values of power and potential difference. For example, it could be 60 W, 220 V. It means that 220 V should be applied across this bulb, and when 220 V is applied, the power consumed will be 60 W. You will find similar markings on all electric appliances. For an electric appliance, the values of power and voltage taken together form what is called the rating of the appliance.

From the rating of an appliance, you can easily calculate its resistance by using the equation $P = V^2/R$. Note that higher the power rating, smaller the resistance. So, a 1000-W heater has less resistance than a 100-W bulb. You can also calculate the current drawn by an appliance by using the relation $i = P/V$.

EXAMPLE 4.8 An electric kettle is rated 500 W, 220 V. It is used to heat water for 30 seconds. Assuming the voltage to be 220 V, calculate the heat produced.

Solution   Since the voltage is 220 V, the power consumed is $P = 500$ W. The heat produced in 30 seconds is
$$U = Pt = (500 \text{ W}) \times (30 \text{ s}) = 15,000 \text{ J}.$$

Kilowatt hour

We have seen that power is the rate of energy consumed or produced. If 1 joule of energy is used per second, we say that energy is used at the rate of 1 watt. In other words, if energy is used at the rate of 1 watt, the total energy used in 1 second is 1 joule. How much energy is used in 1 hour if it is used at the rate of 1000 watts? It is

$$(1000 \text{ watts}) \times (3600 \text{ seconds}) = 3,600,000 \text{ joules}.$$

This amount of energy is called 1 kilowatt hour, written in short as kWh. Thus,

$$1 \text{ kWh} = 3,600,000 \text{ J} = 3.6 \times 10^6 \text{ J}.$$

The electrical energy used in houses, factories, etc., is measured in kilowatt hours. The cost of electricity is fixed per kilowatt hour. One kilowatt hour of electrical energy is often called one unit.

EXAMPLE 4.9 The rate of electricity in a town is Rs 3.00 per unit. Calculate the cost of running an 80-watt fan for ten hours a day for the whole month of June.

Solution   Total time for which the fan is used is (10 hours) × 30 = 300 hours.
The power consumed is (80 W) × (300 hours) = 24000 watt hours = 24 kilowatt hours, or 24 units.
The cost of this power = (Rs 3.00/unit) × (24 units) = Rs 72.

· SOLVED PROBLEMS ·

EXAMPLE 1 How much work will be done in bringing a charge of 5.0 millicoulombs from infinity to a point P at which the potential is 12 V?

Solution   The potential at infinity is usually taken as zero. So, the work done is
$$W = QV = (5.0 \times 10^{-3} \text{ C}) \times (12 \text{ V}) = 60 \times 10^{-3} \text{ J} = 0.06 \text{ J}.$$

EXAMPLE 2   A particle with a charge of 1.5 coulombs is taken from a point A at a potential of 50 V to another point B at a potential of 120 V. Calculate the work done.

Solution   We have $W = Q(V_B - V_A)$
$$= (1.5 \text{ C}) \times (120 \text{ V} - 50 \text{ V}) = (1.5 \times 70) \text{ J} = 105 \text{ J}.$$

EXAMPLE 3   How many electrons are required to get 1 C of negative charge?

Solution   Each electron has a negative charge of $1.6 \times 10^{-19} \text{C}$.
So, the number of electrons for 1 C of negative charge is
$$n = \frac{1 \text{ C}}{1.6 \times 10^{-19} \text{ C}} = 6.25 \times 10^{18}.$$

EXAMPLE 4   Calculate the current in a wire if 900 C of charge passes through it in 10 minutes.

Solution $$i = \frac{Q}{t} = \frac{900 \text{ C}}{10 \times 60 \text{ s}} = 1.5 \text{ A}.$$

EXAMPLE 5   How much current will flow through a resistor of resistance 12 Ω if a battery of 18 V is connected across it?

Solution   From Ohm's law, $i = \dfrac{V}{R} = \dfrac{18 \text{ V}}{12 \, \Omega} = 1.5 \text{ A}.$

EXAMPLE 6   Calculate the resistance of a copper wire of length 1 m and area of cross section 2 mm². Resistivity of copper is 1.7×10^{-8} Ω m.

Solution $$R = \rho \frac{l}{A} = (1.7 \times 10^{-8} \, \Omega \text{ m}) \times \frac{1 \text{ m}}{2 \times (10^{-3} \text{ m})^2} = 8.5 \times 10^{-3} \, \Omega.$$

EXAMPLE 7   A copper wire has a resistance of 0.5 Ω. Another copper wire of the same mass as the first one is double in length of the first. Find the resistance of the second wire.

Solution   For the first wire, let
$$l = \text{length and } A_1 = \text{cross-sectional area.}$$
For the second wire,
$$2l = \text{length and } A_2 = \text{cross-sectional area.}$$
Now, density = mass/volume.

The two wires have the same mass and they have the same density (being made of the same material). So, their volumes are equal.

∴ $lA_1 = 2lA_2$

or $A_1 = 2A_2,$

Let the resistivity of copper be ρ.

Resistance of the first wire is $0.6 \, \Omega = \rho \dfrac{l}{A_1}$ ...(i)

Resistance of the second wire is $R = \rho \dfrac{2l}{A_2}$ ...(ii)

Dividing (ii) by (i),
$$\frac{R}{0.6 \, \Omega} = \frac{2lA_1}{lA_2} = \frac{2(2A_2)}{A_2} = 4$$

∴ $R = 0.6 \, \Omega \times 4 = 2.4 \, \Omega.$

EXAMPLE 8   In an experiment to verify Ohm's law, the current through a resistor and the potential difference across it are measured. From the values given below, plot a graph of i versus V. Show that the data confirms Ohm's law, and find the resistance of the resistor.

| Current (A) | 0.1 0.2 0.3 0.4 |
| Potential difference (V) | 1.2 2.4 3.6 4.8 |

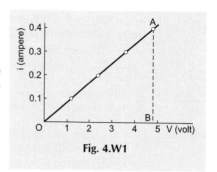

Fig. 4.W1

Solution   The graph is shown in Figure 4.W1. Scales are chosen to cover the given maximum values. We see that the graph is a straight line passing through the origin.

Thus, $i \propto V$, which is Ohm's law. The resistance is

$$R = \frac{V}{i} = \frac{OB}{AB} = \frac{4.8\,V}{0.4\,A} = 12\,\Omega.$$

EXAMPLE 9   When a potential difference of 20 V is applied across a resistor, it draws a current of 3 A. If 30 V is applied across the same resistor, what will be the current?

Solution   The resistance of the resistor is

$$R = \frac{V}{i} = \frac{20\,V}{3\,A} = \frac{20}{3}\,\Omega.$$

When 30 V is applied across the resistor,

$$i = \frac{V}{R} = \frac{30\,V}{20/3\,\Omega} = 4.5\,A.$$

EXAMPLE 10   How will the resistance of a wire change if its diameter (*d*) is doubled, its length remaining the same?

Solution   The cross-sectional area of the wire is $A_1 = \pi r^2 = \pi \left(\frac{d}{2}\right)^2 = \frac{\pi d^2}{4}$.

Its resistance $= R_1 = \rho \frac{l}{A_1} = \rho \frac{l}{\frac{\pi d^2}{4}} = \frac{4\rho l}{\pi d^2}$.

When the diameter is doubled, cross-sectional area $A_2 = \pi \left(\frac{2d}{2}\right)^2 = \pi d^2$.

Its resistance $= R_2 = \rho \frac{l}{A_2} = \rho \frac{l}{\pi d^2}$.

Thus,

$$\frac{R_2}{R_1} = \frac{\frac{\rho l}{\pi d^2}}{\frac{4\rho l}{\pi d^2}} = \frac{1}{4}$$

or

$$R_2 = \frac{1}{4} R_1.$$

So, on doubling the diameter, the area of cross section becomes 4 times and the resistance becomes one-fourth of the initial value.

EXAMPLE 11   Calculate the potential difference across each resistor in the circuit shown in Figure 4.W2.

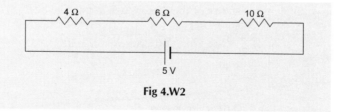

Fig 4.W2

Solution   The three resistors are joined in series. Their equivalent resistance is

$$R = 4\,\Omega + 6\,\Omega + 10\,\Omega = 20\,\Omega.$$

The current through the cell is $i = \frac{5\,V}{20\,\Omega} = 0.25\,A.$

The same current passes through each resistor. Using Ohm's law, the potential difference
across the 4-Ω resistor = 0.25 A $\times$ 4 Ω = 1 V,
across the 6-Ω resistor = 0.25 A $\times$ 6 Ω = 1.5 V, and
across the 10-Ω resistor = 0.25 A $\times$ 10 Ω = 2.5 V.

EXAMPLE 12   **Three identical bulbs are connected in parallel with a battery. The current drawn from the battery is 6 A. If one of the bulbs gets fused, what will be the total current drawn from the battery?**

Solution   Let the potential difference maintained by the battery be V, and let the resistance of each bulb be R (Figure 4.W3a). If the equivalent resistance of the circuit is r,

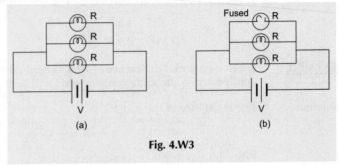

$$\frac{1}{r} = \frac{1}{R} + \frac{1}{R} + \frac{1}{R}$$

or $r = \dfrac{R}{3}.$

Fig. 4.W3

The current is $i = \dfrac{V}{r} = \dfrac{3V}{R}.$ It is given that this current is 6 A.

So, $6\ \text{A} = \dfrac{3V}{R}$ or $\dfrac{V}{R} = 2\ \text{A}.$

If one of the bulbs gets fused (Figure 4.W3b), only two bulbs remain connected in parallel. The equivalent resistance r' in that case is given by

$$\frac{1}{r'} = \frac{1}{R} + \frac{1}{R} \qquad \text{or} \qquad r' = \frac{R}{2}.$$

The current in the battery will be

$$i' = \frac{V}{r'} = \frac{2V}{R} = 2 \times (2\ \text{A}) = 4\ \text{A}.$$

Alternative
As the three bulbs are identical, they will draw equal currents. As the total current is 6 A, each bulb will draw 2 A of current. When one bulb gets fused, there is no current through it. Each of the remaining bulbs remains connected to the battery as before. So, current through each is still 2 A, giving a total current of 4 A through the battery.

EXAMPLE 13   **A uniform wire of resistance R is cut into three equal pieces, and these pieces are joined in parallel. What is the resistance of the combination?**

Solution   Resistance of the wire is $R = \rho \dfrac{l}{A}.$

Resistance of a piece of length $\dfrac{l}{3}$ is $R' = \rho \dfrac{l}{3A}$

or, $R' = \dfrac{R}{3}.$

Let the equivalent resistance of the three wires in parallel be R_p. Then,

$$\frac{1}{R_\text{p}} = \frac{1}{R/3} + \frac{1}{R/3} + \frac{1}{R/3} = \frac{3}{R} + \frac{3}{R} + \frac{3}{R} = \frac{9}{R}.$$

$\therefore$ $R_\text{p} = \dfrac{R}{9}.$

EXAMPLE 14   Consider the circuit shown in Figure 4.W4. The voltmeter on the left reads 10 V and that on the right reads 8 V. Find (a) the current through the resistance R, (b) the value of R, and (c) the potential difference across the battery.

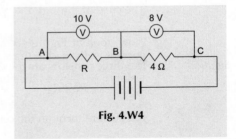

Fig. 4.W4

Solution   (a) Apply Ohm's law to the 4-Ω resistor. The current through this resistor is

$$i = \frac{8\text{ V}}{4\text{ Ω}} = 2\text{ A}.$$

As the two resistors are connected in series, the same current passes through the two resistors (the voltmeters draw only a negligible current). Hence, the current through R is 2 A.

(b) Applying Ohm's law to the resistance R,

$$10\text{ V} = R \times (2\text{ A}) \qquad \text{or} \qquad R = \frac{10\text{ V}}{2\text{ A}} = 5\text{ Ω}.$$

(c) The potential difference across the battery is

$$V_A - V_C = (V_A - V_B) + (V_B - V_C) = 10\text{ V} + 8\text{ V} = 18\text{ V}.$$

EXAMPLE 15 Three resistors of resistances 10 Ω, 20 Ω and 30 Ω are connected in parallel with a 6-V cell. Find (a) the current through each resistor, (b) the currrent supplied by the cell, and (c) the equivalent resistance of the circuit.

Solution   (a) Let the current through the 10-Ω, 20-Ω and 30-Ω resistors be i_1, i_2 and i_3 respectively. The potential difference across each of them is 6 V. Thus,

$$i_1 = \frac{6\text{ V}}{10\text{ Ω}} = 0.6\text{ A} \qquad i_2 = \frac{6\text{ V}}{20\text{ Ω}} = 0.3\text{ A} \qquad i_3 = \frac{6\text{ V}}{30} = 0.2\text{ A}$$

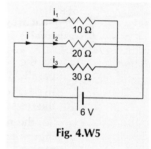

(b) The current supplied by the cell is

$$i = i_1 + i_2 + i_3$$
$$= 0.6\text{ A} + 0.3\text{ A} + 0.2\text{ A} = 1.1\text{ A}.$$

(c) The equivalent resistance of the circuit is

$$R = \frac{V}{i} = \frac{6\text{ V}}{1.1\text{ A}} \approx 5.5\text{ Ω}.$$

Fig. 4.W5

Alternative

$$\frac{1}{R} = \frac{1}{10\text{ Ω}} + \frac{1}{20\text{ Ω}} + \frac{1}{30\text{ Ω}} = \frac{11}{60\text{ Ω}}; \qquad \therefore \ R = \frac{60\text{ Ω}}{11} \approx 5.5\text{ Ω}.$$

EXAMPLE 16 Consider the circuit shown in Figure 4.W6a. Calculate the current through the 3-Ω resistor.

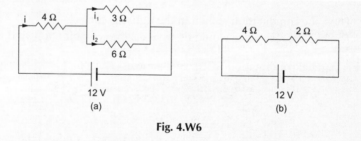

Fig. 4.W6

Solution   The 3-Ω resistor and the 6-Ω resistor are joined in parallel. Their equivalent resistance is

$$R = \frac{(3\text{ Ω}) \times (6\text{ Ω})}{(3\text{ Ω}) + (6\text{ Ω})} = 2\text{ Ω}.$$

Thus, the two resistors may be replaced by a single resistor of resistance 2 Ω. The circuit can be redrawn as shown in Figure 4.W6b. The two resistors in the figure are joined in series. The equivalent resistance is 4 Ω + 2 Ω = 6 Ω.

The current through the battery is $i = \dfrac{12\text{ V}}{6\text{ Ω}} = 2\text{ A}.$

Now, look at Figure 4.W6a. The current through the battery and the 4-Ω resistor is 2 A. This current is divided in the two resistors (3 Ω and 6 Ω) which are joined in parallel.

Using $i_1 = \dfrac{R_2 i}{R_1 + R_2}$, the current through the 3-Ω resistor is

$$i_1 = \frac{(6\text{ Ω}) \times (2\text{ A})}{(3\text{ Ω}) + (6\text{ Ω})} = \frac{12\text{ Ω A}}{9\text{ Ω}} = 1.33\text{ A}.$$

EXAMPLE 17   When two resistors are joined in series, the equivalent resistance is 90 Ω. When the same resistors are joined in parallel, the equivalent resistance is 20Ω. Calculate the resistances of the two resistors.

Solution $R_1 + R_2 = 90\,\Omega$ ... (i)

and $\dfrac{R_1 R_2}{R_1 + R_2} = 20\,\Omega.$ ... (ii)

$\therefore$ $R_1 R_2 = (R_1 + R_2)(20\,\Omega) = (90\,\Omega)(20\,\Omega) = 1800\,\Omega^2.$

Using the relation $(a - b)^2 = (a + b)^2 - 4ab,$

$$R_1 - R_2 = \sqrt{(R_1 + R_2)^2 - 4R_1 R_2}$$
$$= \sqrt{8100\,\Omega^2 - 7200\,\Omega^2} = \sqrt{900\,\Omega^2}$$

$\therefore$ $R_1 - R_2 = 30\,\Omega.$ ... (iii)

From (i) and (iii), $R_1 = 60\,\Omega, R_2 = 30\,\Omega.$

EXAMPLE 18   (a) How will you join three resistors of resistances 4 Ω, 6 Ω and 12 Ω to get an equivalent resistance of 8Ω?
(b) What would be the highest and the lowest equivalent resistances possible by joining these resistors?

Solution   (a) As the equivalent resistance is 8 Ω, the 12-Ω resistor cannot be in series. So, it must be in parallel with some other resistors.
In parallel connection, the equivalent resistance (8Ω) has to be less than all the resistances. So, the resistors of 4 Ω and 6 Ω cannot be in parallel at one time with 12Ω.
So, the resistors have to be in a mixed combination. Let us try the combination shown in Figure 4.W7.
The equivalent resistance of the resistors in parallel between B and C is

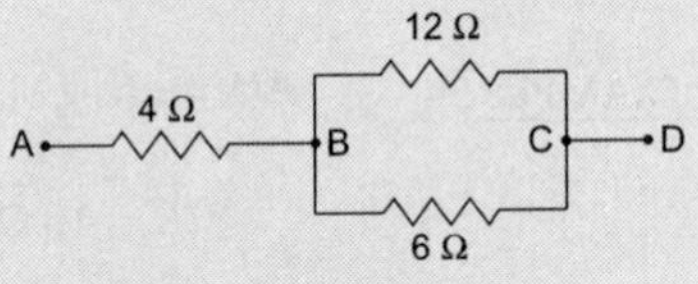

$$\frac{(6\,\Omega) \times (12\,\Omega)}{(6\,\Omega) + (12\,\Omega)} = 4\,\Omega.$$

Fig. 4.W7

So, the resistance between A and D is

$$4\,\Omega + 4\,\Omega = 8\,\Omega.$$

Thus, the combination shown in the figure is correct.
(b) The highest resistance would be from a series combination, and is equal to
$$4\,\Omega + 6\,\Omega + 12\,\Omega = 22\,\Omega.$$
A parallel combination will give the lowest resistance, which is given by

$$\frac{1}{R} = \frac{1}{4\,\Omega} + \frac{1}{6\,\Omega} + \frac{1}{12\,\Omega} = \frac{3 + 2 + 1}{12\,\Omega} = \frac{6}{12\,\Omega}.$$

$\therefore$ $R = 2\,\Omega.$

EXAMPLE 19   How many bulbs of resistance 6 ohms should be joined in parallel to draw a current of 2 amperes from a battery of 3 volts?

Solution   The equivalent rresistance of the circuit $= R = \dfrac{V}{i} = \dfrac{3\,\text{V}}{2\,\text{A}} = 1.5\,\Omega.$

Let n bulbs be joined in parallel to achieve this resistance. Then,

$$\frac{1}{1.5\,\Omega} = \frac{1}{r_1} + \frac{1}{r_2} + \ldots + \frac{1}{r_n} = \frac{n}{6\,\Omega} \qquad \text{(as all resistances} = 6\,\Omega)$$

$\therefore$ $n = \dfrac{6\,\Omega}{1.5\,\Omega} = 4.$

So, 4 bulbs should be connected in parallel.

EXAMPLE 20   A current of 4 A passes through a resistance of 100 Ω for 15 minutes. Calculate the heat produced in calories.

Solution   The heat produced is $U = i^2 Rt$

$$= (4\,\text{A})^2 \times (100\,\Omega) \times (15 \times 60\,\text{s}) = 1.44 \times 10^6\,\text{J}.$$

Now, $4.186 \text{ J} = 1 \text{ cal.}$

Thus, $1.44 \times 10^6 \text{ J} = \dfrac{1.44 \times 10^6}{4.186} \text{ cal} = 3.4 \times 10^5 \text{ cal.}$

EXAMPLE 21   A 12-V battery is connected to a bulb. The battery sends a current of 2.5 A through it. Calculate (a) the power delivered to the bulb, and (b) the energy transferred to the bulb in 5 minutes.

Solution   (a) The power delivered is
$$P = Vi = (12 \text{ V}) \times (2.5 \text{ A}) = 30 \text{ W.}$$
(b) Energy transferred in 5 minutes is
$$U = P \times t = (30 \text{ W}) \times (5 \times 60 \text{ s}) = 9000 \text{ J.}$$

EXAMPLE 22   A current is passed through a resistor for some time. It produces 400 cal of heat in this period. If the current is doubled, how much heat will be produced for the same duration?

Solution   The heat produced is $U = i^2 R t$

or $400 \text{ cal} = i^2 R t.$ ... (i)

If the heat produced is U_1 when the current is doubled, $U_1 = (2i)^2 R t.$ ... (ii)

From (i) and (ii), we have $\dfrac{U_1}{400 \text{ cal}} = \dfrac{(2i)^2 R t}{i^2 R t} = 4$

or $U_1 = 1600 \text{ cal.}$

EXAMPLE 23   Calculate the wattage of an electric heater which draws 5 A current when connected to a 220-V power supply.

Solution   The wattage is $P = Vi = (220 \text{ A}) \times (5 \text{ A}) = 1100 \text{ W.}$

EXAMPLE 24   A bulb draws 24 W when connected to a 12-V supply. Find the power if it is connected to a 6-V supply. (Neglect resistance change due to unequal heating in the two cases.)

Solution   We have $P = \dfrac{V^2}{R}$

or $24 \text{ W} = \dfrac{(12 \text{ V})^2}{R}.$ ... (i)

Suppose the bulb draws power P_1 when connected to the 6-V battery. Then,
$$P_1 = \dfrac{(6 \text{ V})^2}{R}.$$ ... (ii)

From (i) and (ii), we have
$$\dfrac{P_1}{24 \text{ W}} = \dfrac{(6 \text{ V})^2}{(12 \text{ V})^2} = \dfrac{1}{4}$$

or $P_1 = \dfrac{24 \text{ W}}{4} = 6 \text{ W.}$

EXAMPLE 25   Two identical resistors of resistance R are connected in series with a battery of potential difference V for time t. The resistors are later connected in parallel and the same battery is connected across the combination for time t. Compare the heat produced in the two cases.

Solution   The equivalent resistance of the series combination $= R_1 = R + R = 2R.$

The heat produced in time t is $H_1 = \dfrac{V^2}{2R} t.$

The equivalent resistance of the parallel combination is
$$R_2 = \dfrac{(R)(R)}{R + R} = \dfrac{R^2}{2R} = \dfrac{R}{2}.$$

The heat produced in time t is $H_2 = \dfrac{V^2}{R/2} t = \dfrac{4V^2}{R} t.$

The heat produced with the parallel combination is four times that with the series combination.

EXAMPLE 26   A bulb is rated 40 W, 220 V. Find the current drawn by it when it is connected to a 220-V supply.

Solution   Since the bulb is rated at 220 V and it is connected to a 220-V supply, the power consumed will be 40 W. The current drawn by it is

$$i = \frac{P}{V} = \frac{40 \text{ W}}{220 \text{ V}} = \frac{2}{11} \text{ A.}$$

EXAMPLE 27   A bulb is rated 60 W, 240 V. Calculate its resistance when it is on. If the voltage drops to 192 V, what will be the power consumed and the current drawn?

Solution   Power, $P = \dfrac{V^2}{R}$.

$\therefore$ $R = \dfrac{V^2}{P} = \dfrac{(240 \text{ V})^2}{60 \text{ W}} = 960 \text{ } \Omega.$

When the voltage drops to 192 V, the power consumed will be

$$P = \frac{V^2}{R} = \frac{(192 \text{ V})^2}{960 \text{ } \Omega} = 38.4 \text{ W.}$$

The current drawn will be $i = \dfrac{V}{R} = \dfrac{192 \text{ V}}{960 \text{ } \Omega} = 0.2 \text{ A.}$

EXAMPLE 28   A room has two tube lights, a fan and a TV. Each tube light draws 40 W, the fan draws 80 W, and the TV draws 60 W. On the average, the tube lights are kept on for five hours, the fan for twelve hours and the TV for eight hours every day. The rate for electrical energy is Rs 3.10 per kWh. Calculate the cost of electricity used in this room in a 30-day month.

Solution   For each tube light, power $P = 40 \text{ W} = \dfrac{40}{1000}$ kW. So, the energy consumed by each tube light in a day is

$$U = P \times t = \left(\frac{40}{1000} \text{ kW} \right) \times (5 \text{ h}) = 0.2 \text{ kWh.}$$

Energy consumed by the fan in a day is
$$U = P \times t = (80 \text{ W}) \times (12 \text{ h}) = 0.96 \text{ kWh.}$$

Energy consumed by the TV in a day is
$$U = P \times t = (60 \text{ W}) \times (8 \text{ h}) = 0.48 \text{ kWh.}$$

Total energy consumed in a day is
$$2 \times 0.2 \text{ kWh} + 0.96 \text{ kWh} + 0.48 \text{ kWh} = 1.84 \text{ kWh.}$$

Energy consumed in a month is
$$(1.84 \text{ kWh}) \times 30 = 55.2 \text{ kWh.}$$
The cost of electricity $= \text{Rs } (55.2 \times 3.1) = \text{Rs } 171.12.$

· POINTS TO REMEMBER ·

- *Potential*

  The potential difference between two points A and B is the work done per unit charge in taking a charge from B to A. $V = V_A - V_B = W/q$.

  The potential at a point is the work done per unit charge in taking a charge to that point from a chosen reference point. Quite often, the potential at infinity is chosen as zero. The SI unit of potential and potential difference is the volt (V).

- *Electric current*

  A free-to-move positive charge will move from higher to lower potential. A negative charge will move from lower to higher potential.

The flow of charge is called current. The charge passing per unit time through a given place is the magnitude of the electric current at that place. The SI unit of current is the ampere (A). If one coulomb of charge passes through a place in one second, the current there is 1 A.

- *Ohm's law*

  The current through a metallic element is proportional to the potential difference applied between its ends, provided the temperature remains constant. $V = iR$, where R is the resistance of the element.

  The SI unit of resistance is the ohm (Ω). If a potential difference of 1 volt is applied across an element, and a current of 1 ampere passes through it, the resistance of the element is called 1 ohm.

The resistance of a wire is directly proportional to its length and inversely proportional to its area of cross section. The resistance of a wire also depends on the material. It increases slightly with increase in temperature.

- *Combination of resistors*

Two or more resistors are said to be connected in series if the current flowing through one also flows through the rest. The total potential difference across the combination is equal to the sum of the potential differences across the individual resistors.

If resistors are connected in such a way that the same potential difference gets applied to each of them, they are said to be connected in parallel. The total current flowing into the combination is equal to the sum of the currents through the individual resistors.

- *Heating effect of electric current*

When an electric current passes through a wire, the heat produced is proportional to the square of the current, the resistance of the wire and the time for which the current flows.

The common unit of electrical energy is the kilowatt hour.

The electrical energy produced or consumed per unit time is called *electric power*.

- *Mathematical relations*

Ohm's law	$i = \dfrac{Q}{t}$ $V = iR$ $R = \rho \dfrac{l}{A}$
Resistors in series	$R_{eq} = R_1 + R_2 + R_3 +$
Resistors in parallel	$\dfrac{1}{R_{eq}} = \dfrac{1}{R_1} + \dfrac{1}{R_2} + \dfrac{1}{R_3} +$
Heat produced by electric current	$U = i^2 Rt = \dfrac{V^2}{R} t = Vit$
Electric power	$P = \dfrac{U}{t} = i^2 R = \dfrac{V^2}{R} = Vi$

· EXERCISES ·

A. *Very-Short-Answer Questions*

1. Write the unit of electric potential.
2. Define the potential at a point.
3. Define the potential difference between two points.
4. A dry cell usually has a small cap at one end and a flat surface at the other end. Which of the two is at a higher potential?
5. Name the instruments used to measure electric current and potential difference respectively. Which of these is connected in series and which is connected in parallel in a circuit?
6. What is the shape of the graph between V and i, where V is the potential difference between the ends of a wire and i is the current in it?
7. Consider the units volt, ohm and ampere. One of them is the same as the product of the other two. Which one is this?
8. Name three electrical appliances in which the heating effect of electric current is used.
9. Two bulbs have ratings 100 W, 220 V and 60 W, 220 V. Which one has a greater resistance?
10. You have two resistors of resistances 30 Ω and 60 Ω. What resistances can you get by combining the two?
11. Draw a diagram to show two resistors R_1 and R_2 connected in series. **(2006)**
12. Two resistors of 5 Ω and 10 Ω are connected in series in a circuit. How does the current passing through them compare? **(2006)**
13. A wire of resistance 10 Ω is bent to form a closed circle. What is the resistance across a diameter of the circle? **(2005)**

B. *Short-Answer Questions*

1. What is the difference between a conductor and an insulator? Give one example of each.
2. The current in a wire is one ampere. Explain this statement in terms of the charge flowing through the wire.
3. When do you say that the resistance of a wire is 1 Ω?
4. Draw a circuit diagram for a circuit in which two resistors A and B are joined in series with a battery, and a voltmeter is connected to measure the potential difference across the resistor A.
5. When are resistors said to be connected in series?
6. When are resistors said to be connected in parallel?
7. Why is tungsten suitable for making the filament of a bulb?
8. Why is tungsten not used as a fuse wire?
9. Alloys are preferred over metals for making the heating element of heaters. Why?
10. Silver is a better conductor of electricity than copper. Why then do we use copper wire for conducting electricity?

C. *Long-Answer Questions*

1. State Ohm's law. How can it be verified?
2. When the terminals of a cell are connected to the ends of an iron rod, electric current flows through

the rod. When the terminals are connected to the ends of a wooden rod, no current flows. Explain why, when the wooden rod also has a large number of electrons.

3. Define electric current and state its unit. How can Ohm's law be used to define ohm?

4. Deduce the expression for the equivalent resistance of the parallel combination of two resistances R_1 and R_2.

5. Deduce the expression for the equivalent resistance of the two resistances R_1 and R_2 connected in series.

6. Derive an expression for the heat produced in time t in a wire of resistance R, which is carrying a current i.

D. Numerical Problems

1. When a particle of charge 10 µC is brought from infinity to a point P, 2.0 mJ of work is done by the external forces. What is the potential at P ?

2. Calculate the work done in taking a charge of 0.02 C from A to B if the potential at A is 20 V, and that at B is 30 V.

3. How much charge flows through a wire in 10 minutes if the current through it is 2.5 A?

4. A 2-V cell is connected to a 1-Ω resistor. How many electrons come out of the negative terminal of the cell in 2 minutes?

5. The amount of charge passing through a cell in 4 seconds is 12 C. What is the current supplied by the cell?

6. A 6-V battery is connected across a 5-Ω resistor. Calculate the current passing through the resistor.

7. When a 24-V battery is connected to a resistor, the current in it is 0.4 A. What is the resistance of the resistor? What would be the current through it when it is connected to a battery of 6 V?

8. In an experiment, the current flowing through a resistor and the potential difference across it are measured. The values are given below. Show that these values confirm Ohm's law, and find the resistance of the resistor.

i (ampere)	1.0	1.5	2.0	2.5	3.0
V (volt)	4.0	6.0	8.0	10.0	12

9. The resitivity of copper is 1.7×10^{-8} Ω m. (a) What length of copper wire of diameter 0.1 mm will have a resistance of 34 Ω? (b) Another copper wire of the same length but of half the diameter as the first is taken. What is the ratio of its resistance to that of the first wire?

10. Three resistors, each of resistance 12 Ω, are connected in parallel. What is the equivalent resistance?

11. A uniform wire of resistance R is cut into two equal pieces, and these pieces are joined in parallel. What is the resistance of the combination?

12. You have three resisters of 9 ohms each. By combining them what can be (a) the highest resistance, and (b) the lowest resistance? (c) How can you combine them to get a resistance of 12 Ω?

13. How will you join the resistors of resistances 3 Ω, 6 Ω and 8 Ω to get an equivalent resistance of 10 Ω?

14. Find the current through the circuit shown in Figure 4.E1. Also, find the potential difference across the 20-Ω resistor.

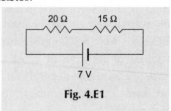

Fig. 4.E1

15. Find (a) the equivalent resistance, (b) the current passing through the cell, and (c) the current passing through the 30-Ω resistor in the circuit shown in Figure 4.E2.

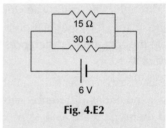

Fig. 4.E2

16. Find the current supplied by the cell in the circuit shown in Figure 4.E3.

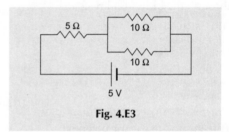

Fig. 4.E3

17. In the circuit shown below, calculate the total resistance of the circuit and the current flowing through it.   **(2005)**

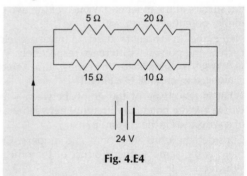

Fig. 4.E4

18. Figure 4.E5 shows a part of an electric circuit. The reading of the ammeter is 3.0 A. Find the currents through the 10-Ω and 20-Ω resistors.

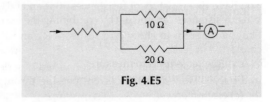

Fig. 4.E5

19. A 12-V battery connected to a bulb drives a current of 2.0 A through it. Find the energy supplied by the battery in 10 minutes.

20. A current of 1.5 A flows through a wire of 8 Ω. Find the amount of heat produced in 10 seconds.

21. A current of 2 A produces 200 J of heat in a wire in a given period of time. If the current is increased to 4 A, how much heat will be produced in the same time?

22. A bulb is rated 5.0 V, 100 mA. Calculate its rated power and resistance. **(2006)**

23. Calculate the resistance of a bulb rated 40 W, 230 V when in ON condition.

24. Calculate the current passing through a bulb rated 60 W, 240 V when it is connected to a 240-V power supply.

25. Two resistors of resistances 10 Ω and 20 Ω are joined in series. A potential difference of 12 V is applied across the combination. Find the power consumed by each resistor.

26. Two resistors of resistances 10 Ω and 20 Ω are joined in parallel. A potential difference of 12 V is applied across the combination. Find the power consumed by each resistor.

27. Calculate the energy consumed in kilowatt hours by a 60-W fan in 2 hours.

28. A heater draws 1100 W at 220 V. (a) Find the resistance of the heater when in ON condition. (b) Calculate the kilowatt hours consumed in a week if the heater is used daily for four hours at the rated voltage.

29. A bulb used in a car is rated 12 V, 48 W. Find the energy consumed in one minute when the bulb is connected to (a) a 12-V battery, and (b) a 6-V battery.

E. *Objective Questions*

I. *Pick the correct option.*

1. The potential at a point is 20 V. The work done in bringing a charge of 0.5 C from infinity to this point will be
   (a) 20 J (b) 10 J
   (c) 5 J (d) 40 J

2. A negative charge released from a point A moves along the line AB. The potential at A is 15 V, and it varies uniformly along AB. The potential at B
   (a) may be 10 V (b) may be 15 V
   (c) may be 20 V (d) must be 15 V

3. A charge is taken from a point A to a point B. The work done per unit charge in the process is called
   (a) the potential at A
   (b) the potential at B
   (c) the potential difference between B and A
   (d) the current from A to B

4. Joule/coulomb is the same as
   (a) watt (b) volt
   (c) ampere (d) ohm

5. A voltmeter is used to measure
   (a) potential difference (b) electric current
   (c) electric power (d) resistance

6. On which of the following no 'plus' or 'minus' sign is marked?
   (a) a cell (b) an ammeter
   (c) a voltmeter (d) a resistor

7. An ammeter is always connected in ...... and a voltmeter in .... The suitable words, in order, for the blanks are
   (a) series; series (b) parallel; parallel
   (c) parallel; series (d) series; parallel

8. In a metal,
   (a) all the electrons are free to move
   (b) all the electrons are bound to their parent atoms
   (c) there are no electrons
   (d) some electrons are free to move

9. The free electrons of a metal are free to
   (a) move on the surface only
   (b) are free to escape through the surface
   (c) are free to fall into the nuclei
   (d) are free to move anywhere in the metal

10. The current in a wire depends
    (a) only on the potential difference applied
    (b) only on the resistance of the wire
    (c) on both of them
    (d) on none of them

11. Consider the following incomplete statement "Ohm's law relates potential difference with ...... for a given resistance". The suitable choice for the missing word is
    (a) power (b) energy
    (c) current (d) time

12. Consider the following statements:
    A. In series connection, the same current flows through each element.
    B. In parallel connection, the same potential difference gets applied across each element.
    (a) both A and B are correct
    (b) A is correct but B is wrong
    (c) A is wrong but B is correct
    (d) both A and B are wrong

II. *Mark the statements True (T) or False (F).*

1. It is not possible to have a particle with charge 2.0×10^{-19} C.

2. An electron released from rest at a point A moves towards a nearby point B. The potential at A is higher than the potential at B.

3. A metal has a large number of electrons, but a nonmetal has only a small number of electrons.

4. The positive terminal of a cell is connected to the end A, and the negative terminal is connected to the end B of a metallic wire AB. Electrons flow in the wire in the direction B to A.

5. If two equal resistances are connected in parallel, the equivalent resistance is halved.

6. A thick wire has a larger resistance than a thin wire.

III. *Fill in the blanks.*

1. The resistance of a cylindrical piece of rubber is ...... than that of a similar piece of copper.

2. The kilowatt hour is the unit of ....

3. The equivalent resistance of two equal resistances connected in parallel is ...... the value of each resistance.

4. Three resistors are connected in series with a cell. If the current in each resistor is 2 A, that in the cell will be ....

5. Three resistors are connected in parallel with a battery. If the current in each resistor is 2 A, that in the battery will be ....

· ANSWERS ·

D. *Numerical Problems*

1. 200 V   2. 0.2 J   3. 1500 C
4. 1.5×10^{21} electrons   5. 3 A
6. 1.2 A   7. 60 Ω, 0.1 A   8. 4 Ω
9. (a) 15.71 m (b) 4 : 1 (4 times)
10. 4 Ω   11. R/4
12. (a) 27 Ω (b) 3 Ω (c) one resistor connected in series to a combination of two resistors in parallel
13. 8-Ω resistor connected in series to a parallel combination of 6 Ω and 3 Ω
14. 0.2 A, 4 V
15. (a) 10 Ω (b) 0.6 A (c) 0.2 A   16. 0.5 A
17. 12.5 Ω, 1.92 A   18. 2 A, 1 A

19. 14,400 J   20. 180 J or 43 cal
21. 800 J   22. 0.5 W, 50 Ω
23. 1322.5 Ω   24. 0.25 A   25. 1.6 W, 3.2 W
26. 14.4 W, 7.2 W   27. 0.12 kWh
28. (a) 44 Ω (b) 30.8 kWh   29. (a) 2880 J (b) 720 J

E. *Objective Questions*

I.   1. (b)   2. (c)   3. (c)   4. (b)   5. (a)
     6. (d)   7. (d)   8. (d)   9. (d)   10. (c)
    11. (c)   12. (a)
II. 1. T   2. F   3. F   4. T   5. T
     6. F

· POSTSCRIPT ·

Semiconductors

Metals like copper, silver, iron, etc., are conductors of electricity as they contain a large number of free electrons. Rubber, glass, wood, etc., are insulators as they have almost no free electrons. In between the two, there are materials such as silicon and germanium in which the number of free electrons is much greater than that in insulators and much smaller than that in conductors. Such materials are called *semiconductors*. Their resistivity decreases as the temperature increases. Also the resistivity can be drastically changed by putting some 'impurity' in the semiconductor. By controlling the amount of impurity and its distribution, very useful electronic devices are formed from semiconductors. Such semiconductor devices are used in computers, digital watches, electronic calculators, etc.

Xerography

You know about many applications of electric current, but can you name one application of electric charge? Most photocopying machines are based on the properties of electric charges. A photocopying machine has a powerful light source and a system of mirrors and lenses which forms an image of the original document on a roller made of a special

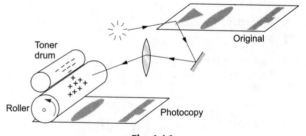

Fig. 4.A1

material. The roller is initially positively charged. The material of the roller has the property of losing its charge when exposed to light. Light reflected from the white portions of the original document falls on the roller and these portions of the drum lose their charge. The dark portions of the original do not reflect light and, therefore, the corresponding areas on the roller retain positive charge. For printing, a negatively charged 'toner' (special type of ink) is used. The positively charged areas on the roller attract the negatively charged toner. As the drum rotates, the toner gets transferred to the paper, which passes in contact with the drum. This way, the dark portions on the original document are imaged on the paper.

5 Magnetic Effect of Electric Current

The works of scientists like Hans Christian Oersted, Michael Faraday and André Ampère showed that there is a definite relationship between electricity and magnetism. Before getting into how electricity and magnetism are related, let us briefly take a look at magnetism.

MAGNETISM

Magnetism has been a source of curiosity for ages. Magnets are commonly found in science laboratories, toys and in the magnetic stickers that we stick to refrigerators and steel *almirahs*. The earth itself acts as a magnet. Actually, magnets are all around us, since each electron, proton and neutron behaves as a tiny magnet. Magnetism has many uses—from the simple magnetic sticker to magnetic resonance imaging (MRI). MRI is a diagnostic technique in which the magnetism of the protons inside the human body is used to form images of tissues.

Magnets

Certain rocks behave as natural magnets. When suspended from a string, they align along the south to north direction. These natural magnets contain magnetite (Fe_3O_4), a magnetic compound. Magnets can also be made artificially by certain methods. Magnets made of certain alloys of iron, nickel and cobalt retain their magnetism for a long time and are, therefore, called permanent magnets. And the material which retains magnetism for a long time is called a hard magnetic material. Alnico (an alloy of aluminium, nickel and cobalt), and certain types of steel like carbon steel and cobalt steel are some hard magnetic materials used for making permanent magnets.

Permanent magnets are made in various shapes such as bar, rod, disc and ring (Figure 5.1a). You also get horseshoe magnets, which are shaped like a horseshoe or the letter U. In bar, rod and horseshoe magnets, the north and south poles are either indicated by the letters N and S, or only the north pole is indicated by a dot. In disc and ring magnets, one face is the north pole while the other is the south pole.

One of the most common uses of a permanent magnet is as a direction-finding compass. A magnetic compass has a small light magnet, called the magnetic needle. The needle can move freely in a horizontal plane. When kept away from other magnets, the north pole of the needle points towards the geographical north of the earth.

(a)

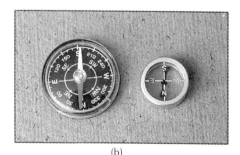
(b)

Fig. 5.1 (a) Magnets of different shapes (b) Magnetic compasses

Magnetic Field

The most striking thing about magnets is the attraction and repulsion between them. How do we explain these forces between two magnets? We say that a magnet produces a magnetic field in the space around it, which exerts a force on any other magnet placed in it. Each point in this field has a particular strength. The field at each point also has a definite direction.

The direction of the magnetic field due to a magnet at a point near it can be found by placing a magnetic compass at that point. The compass needle comes to rest along a particular direction. The direction of the magnetic field at the point is the direction *from* the south pole *to* the north pole of the needle.

When a magnetic compass is kept at a place which is away from all magnets, its needle comes to rest along the north–south direction. This means that the direction of the magnetic field there is from the south to the north. This field is produced by the earth. The magnetic field of the earth also affects a compass needle placed near a magnet. The direction of the compass needle gives the direction of the net magnetic field due to the bar magnet and the earth. However, if the compass is close to the magnet, the contribution due to the earth's field may be neglected.

To find out how the direction of the magnetic field changes at different places near a magnet, do the following activities.

1. Fix a white sheet of paper on a horizontal surface and keep a strong bar magnet on it. Place a small magnetic compass at various points near the magnet, and note the direction in which its needle comes to rest at these points. Figure 5.2a shows these directions at points such as *A, B, C, D, E* and *F*. The direction of the needle at a point gives the direction of the magnetic field at that point.

   Place the compass close to the north pole of the magnet. Once the needle comes to rest, look from above, and with a pencil, mark the position of the north pole of the needle on the sheet (i.e., mark the point closest to the north pole). Now, shift the compass ahead in such a way that after the needle comes to rest, its south pole is at the point marked for the previous position of the north pole. Mark the position of the north pole of the needle at the new location. Keep moving the compass ahead in this way till you reach the south pole of the magnet. Then join all the points marked on the paper with a smooth curve. The curve will look like the dotted line in Figure 5.2a.

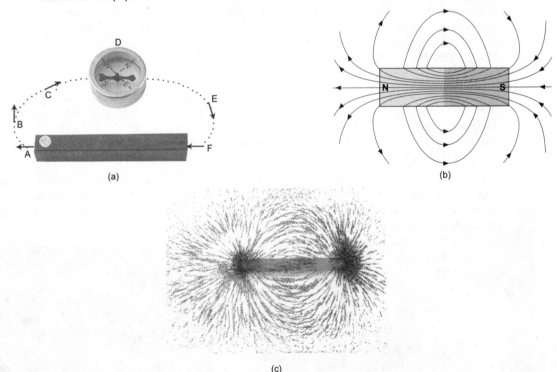

(a)

(b)

(c)

Fig. 5.2 (a) The direction of a magnetic needle at a place near a magnet indicates the direction of the magnetic field at that place. (b) Representation of magnetic field lines around a bar magnet (c) Iron filings arrange themselves along magnetic field lines.

Repeat the whole procedure to get some more curved lines. Each time start from a new position near the north pole of the magnet. If you draw a tangent at any point on these lines, the magnetic field at that point will be along the tangent.

A line such that the tangent at any point on it gives the direction of the magnetic field at that point is called a magnetic field line or magnetic line of force. Figure 5.2b shows some magnetic field lines due to a bar magnet. An arrow showing the direction of the field at a point has been drawn on each field line. Remember that the field lines are imaginary. They just help us visualize magnetic fields.

2. You can see magnetic field lines with the help of iron filings too. Place a glass or clear plastic sheet over a bar magnet. Sprinkle some iron filings over the sheet, and gently tap the sheet. The iron filings will arrange themselves to show the magnetic field lines (Figure 5.2c).

You can make the following observations about magnetic field lines from Figure 5.2b.

(a) All field lines are closed curves. They come out of the magnet from the side of the north pole and go into it on the side of the south pole. They continue inside the magnet too. Although we cannot draw the lines inside the magnet, we know about them from other observations.

(b) The field lines are close together near the poles and spread out away from them. The field is stronger where the field lines are more closely spaced. So, the field is stronger near the poles than at other points.

(c) The field lines never intersect. If two field lines were to intersect then a compass needle placed at the point of intersection would point in two different directions—which is not possible.

AN ELECTRIC CURRENT PRODUCES A MAGNETIC FIELD

A magnet is not the only thing that produces a magnetic field. *An electric current in a conductor also produces a magnetic field.* This was first observed in 1820 by the Danish physicist Hans Christian Oersted (1777–1851). The magnetic effect of electric current can be very easily be demonstrated by bringing a magnetic compass near a current-carrying wire. The compass needle gets deflected, showing that a magnetic field is produced near the wire.

Place a magnetic compass on a wooden or plastic block, away from all magnetic material. When the compass needle comes to rest, fix a wire over the compass, parallel to the needle. Connect the wire to a battery through a switch, as shown in Figure 5.3a. Close the switch to pass a current through the wire. The compass needle will get deflected, and come to rest at right angles to its original position. If the direction of the current is from south to north, the north pole of the needle will come to rest pointing west.

Now, hold the compass above the wire. The needle will get deflected in the opposite direction. The direction of deflection will also change if you reverse the direction of the current in the wire by interchanging the battery connections. If you switch off the current in the wire, the needle will go back to its original position.

Make sure that you pass a current through the wire only for short periods of time (say, 5 seconds). Allowing current to pass through the wire for long will heat the wire considerably and also drain the battery rapidly.

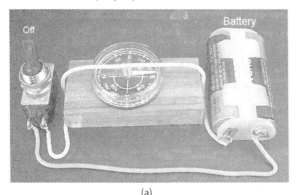
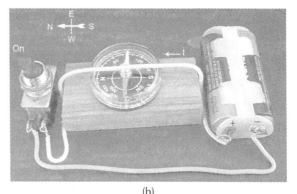

(a)   (b)

Fig. 5.3 A current-carrying wire produces a magnetic field that deflects the needle of the compass.

Magnetic Field Lines due to a Current in a Straight Conductor

The direction of the magnetic field due to a current can be studied by drawing magnetic field lines.

Fix a long stiff wire AB upright in a piece of cardboard kept horizontally. Connect the wire to a battery through a switch, as shown in Figure 5.4a. Use long connecting wires to keep the battery and the switch away from the cardboard. Now, place a compass on the cardboard. Start the current by closing the switch. The compass needle will get deflected, and its direction will show the direction of the magnetic field at that point.

Mark the position of the north pole of the needle on the cardboard. Shift the compass ahead so that the south pole of the needle lies at the point marked for the previous position of the north pole. Mark the new position of the north pole. Repeat the procedure till you reach the point from where you started. Join all the points by a smooth curve to give a field ine. Similarly, draw other field lines at different distances from the wire. Draw arrows on the lines to show the direction of the magnetic field. If the current is strong, say about 2 A, the lines will be nearly circular. If the current is weak, it will produce a weak magnetic field. Then the earth's magnetic field will have greater effect on the field lines, and they will not be circular.

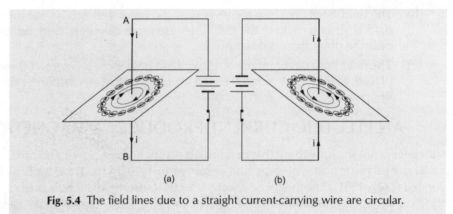

(a)   (b)

Fig. 5.4 The field lines due to a straight current-carrying wire are circular.

If the direction of the current is reversed, the field lines will still be circular, but the directions of the field lines will be reversed (Figure 5.4b). This means, the north pole of the needle will point in the opposite direction.

You can also sprinkle iron filings on the cardboard to see how the field lines are arranged. While a current is passing through the wire, gently tap the cardboard. The iron filings will get arranged in concentric circles, suggesting that the field lines due to a current passing through a straight wire are circular.

Maxwell's Right-hand Thumb Rule

The direction of the magnetic field due to a current in a straight conductor is given by Maxwell's right-hand thumb rule.

If a straight current-carrying wire is imagined to be held in the right hand, with the thumb stretched along the direction of the current, the direction of the magnetic field produced by the current is in the direction in which the fingers are curled (Figure 5.5a).

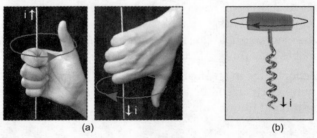

(a)   (b)

Fig. 5.5 (a) Maxwell's right-hand thumb rule and (b) corkscrew rule are two ways of finding the direction of the magnetic field due to a current in a straight wire.

This rule is also called Maxwell's corkscrew rule. Suppose the tip of a rotating corkscrew (or a screw) advances in the direction of the current. Then the direction of rotation of its handle (or head) gives the direction of the current.

Strength of the Magnetic Field due to the Current in a Straight Wire

A compass needle gets deflected when kept near a current-carrying wire. If the current in the wire is increased by applying a greater potential difference across it, the needle gets deflected by a larger angle. This means that the strength of the magnetic field increases with increase in current. In fact, the strength of the magnetic field produced by an electric current is directly proportional to the current.

If you move a compass away from a current-carrying wire, you will notice that as the distance of the compass from the wire increases, the deflection of its needle decreases. This means that the strength of the magnetic field reduces with distance from the wire. For a long, straight current-carrying wire, the strength of the magnetic field is inversely proportional to the distance.

Magnetic Field Lines due to a Current in a Circular Loop

Consider a loop of wire that forms a nearly complete circle. It is fixed vertically in a piece of cardboard, with half the loop above the cardboard and half below it (Figure 5.6a). Join the free ends of the wire to a battery through a switch, and pass a current through it.

The wire passes through the cardboard at two points. Using the procedure discussed before, draw the magnetic field lines around the two points above the cardboard. The lines will be nearly concentric circles centered on the point through which the wire passes. The lines near the centre of the loop are nearly straight. In fact, the magnetic field at the centre of the loop is perpendicular to the plane of the loop, i.e., it is along the axis of the loop. Figure 5.6b shows the pattern with the help of iron filings.

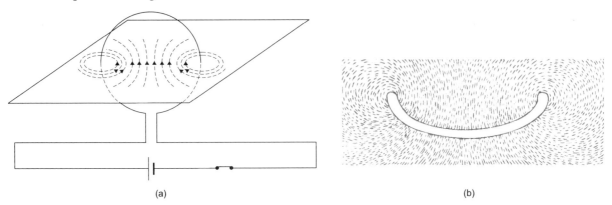

(a)   (b)

Fig. 5.6 The magnetic field lines due to a current-carrying loop can be (a) drawn using a magnetic compass, and (b) shown with the help of iron fillings.

A coil is made by winding several turns of insulated wire in a circular form. When a current passes through a coil, each turn produces its own magnetic field. These fields together give rise to a net magnetic field that is stronger than that produced by a circular loop of single turn. If a coil has n turns, the magnetic field due to the coil is n times stronger than that due to a single turn. In fact, the strength of the magnetic field due to a current-carrying circular coil is proportional to the number of turns and the current.

The direction of the magnetic field (B) at a point on the axis of a current-carrying circular coil or a loop a can be found from the following right-hand thumb rule.

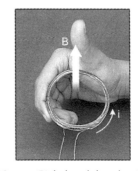

Fig. 5.7 Right-hand thumb rule for loops and coils

If the fingers of the right hand are curled along the direction of the current in a loop, the stretched thumb gives the direction of the magnetic field (Figure 5.7).

Magnetic Field due to a Solenoid

When a long insulated wire is tightly wound in the shape of a spring, with closely spaced turns that lie side by side, we get a solenoid (Figure 5.8a). Generally, a solenoid is made by winding wire over a nonconducting cylindrical tube. A solenoid differs from a circular coil in that the length of the solenoid is much greater than its diameter.

When a current enters a solenoid at one end, it passes through each turn before coming out at the other end. Each turn produces its own magnetic field. The net magnetic field is as represented by the magnetic field lines in Figure 5.8b. Note that the pattern of field lines outside the solenoid is similar to that of a bar magnet (Figure 5.2b). Actually, a current-carrying solenoid behaves like a bar magnet of the same shape. It also has opposite poles at its ends.

The magnetic field inside a long current-carrying solenoid is nearly uniform and is parallel to the axis of the solenoid. This is true for the inner part of the solenoid, away from the ends. Near the ends the magnetic field decreases. Imagine holding the solenoid in your right hand, with the fingers curled along the direction of the current. The direction of the thumb then gives the direction of the magnetic field. It also points towards the end where the north pole of the solenoid appears. Another way of finding the north pole of a solenoid is to check which end gets repelled by the north pole of a bar magnet.

How are the fields of a current-carrying solenoid and coil different? The field inside a current-carrying solenoid is quite uniform for the most part. It only decreases near the ends. The field of a current-carrying coil is not uniform. It changes with distance from the centre.

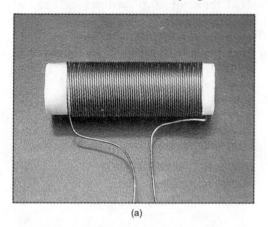

(a)

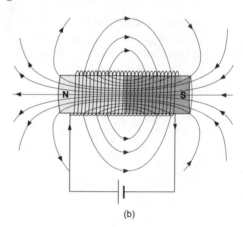

(b)

Fig. 5.8 (a) A solenoid (b) Magnetic field lines due to a solenoid

Electromagnet

An iron nail or a bolt will not attract other iron or steel objects. But what happens if they are placed inside a solenoid carrying a current? Let us find out.

Wind a solenoid directly over an iron bolt or nail, using 5–8 feet of thick enamelled copper wire. (In these wires, the enamel coating acts as the insulator.) Use adhesive tape to keep the turns in place. Scrape off the enamel from the free ends of the wire, and connect them to a battery through a switch. Now, close the switch. The bolt will attract iron and steel objects placed near it. If you turn the current off, the bolt will no longer attract these objects.

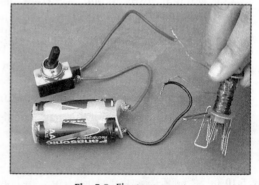

Fig. 5.9 Electromagnet

When a current passes through the solenoid, a magnetic field is produced inside it. The iron bolt (or any other iron object) placed in this field gets magnetized, i.e., it becomes a magnet. However, when the current is switched off, the magnetic field inside the solenoid becomes zero, and the bolt loses its magnetism. A magnet formed temporarily due to the magnetic field of a current is called an electromagnet. Electromagnets have the following properties.

(a) Unlike a permanent magnet, the electromagnet's magnetism is not permanent.

(b) The electromagnet has poles at its ends. However, the end at which a pole appears is not fixed. The poles get interchanged when the direction of current through the solenoid is changed.

The iron used in nails, bolts, etc., is a soft magnetic material, and is called soft iron. Such a material becomes magnetized in a magnetic field, but loses its magnetism once the field is removed. Electromagnets are made by winding wire over a core (such as a rod) made of a soft magnetic material. *This is to ensure that the electromagnet loses its magnetism once the current is switched off.* If you put a rod made of a hard magnetic material such as carbon steel in a magnetic field for some time, the rod will become a permanent magnet. Strong permanent magnets are actually made this way.

A MAGNETIC FIELD EXERTS A FORCE ON A CURRENT-CARRYING CONDUCTOR

We have seen that an electric current produces a magnetic field, which exerts force on a magnet placed near it. What happens when a current-carrying wire is placed in a magnetic field such as that due to a permanent magnet? Let us find out.

Connect the ends of a small, thick aluminium or copper wire to two long, thin wires. Use these wires to hang the aluminium wire from a support. Connect the wires to a battery and switch, as shown in Figure 5.10a. Place a horseshoe magnet as shown. The aluminium wire should swing freely between the poles.

Turn on the switch to pass a current. The aluminium wire will move, showing that the magnetic field exerts a force on it. Note the direction in which the wire moves. Turn the magnet upside down to change the direction of the magnetic field. Now, when a current is passed through the wire, the wire moves in the opposite direction. The direction in which the wire moves also changes if you change the direction of the current by interchanging the connections to the battery.

(In this activity you can also use a disc or ring magnet kept below the wire. And if you have a bar magnet, place it vertically, below the wire.)

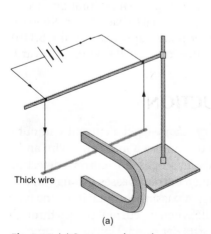
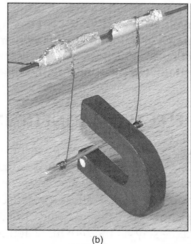
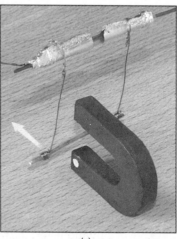

(a)   (b)   (c)

Thick wire

Fig. 5.10 (a) Set up to show that a current-carrying conductor experiences a force in a magnetic field (b) Position of the wire when no current passes through it, and (c) its position when it carries a current

You know that current flows from the positive to the negative terminal of a battery. Also, the direction of the field of a magnet is from the north to the south pole. So, based on your observations in the activity, you can say that the following are true for a current-carrying conductor placed in a magnetic field.

(a)   A current-carrying conductor experiences a force in a magnetic field.

(b)   The direction of the force depends on the direction of the magnetic field and is perpendicular to it.

(c)   The direction of the force depends on the direction of the current and is perpendicular to it.

Fleming's Left-hand Rule

Sir John Ambrose Fleming (1849–1945), an English engineer and professor, suggested a simple rule for finding the direction of the force experienced by a current-carrying wire placed in a magnetic field that is perpendicular to the current in the wire.

> If the forefinger, second finger and thumb of the left hand are stretched at right angles to each other, with the forefinger in the direction of the field and the second finger in the direction of the current then the thumb indicates the direction of the force.

You can remember this rule as follows. The words *Field*, *Current* and *Movement* (of the wire) start with the letters *F*, *C* and *M* respectively. The words *Forefinger*, *seCond* and *thuMb* have these letters in them. So, *Field* is shown by the *Forefinger*, *Current* by the *seCond* finger, and *Movement* by the *thuMb*. Obviously, the movement of the wire denotes the force on it.

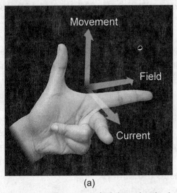
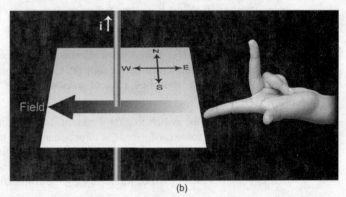

(a)   (b)

Fig. 5.11 Fleming's left-hand rule for the direction of the force on a current-carrying conductor placed in a magnetic field.

Suppose a vertical wire carries a current in the upward direction. Also, suppose that a magnetic field exists from east to west. To apply Fleming's left-hand rule to this situation, stretch the forefinger, second finger and thumb of your left hand at right angles to each other. Keep the hand such that the forefinger points west and the second finger points upwards (Figure 5.11b). You will find that the thumb points towards the south. So, the force on the wire is towards the south.

ELECTROMAGNETIC INDUCTION

So far, we have produced an electric current by using a battery. Can we get a current without a battery? Yes, we can. To produce and detect such a current, you can use a magnet, a wire and a galvanometer (or a galvanoscope). Galvanometers and galvanoscopes are current-detecting instruments. While the needle of a galvanoscope deflects when a current passes through it, in a galvanometer, there is also an arrangement to measure the current passing through it. In one type of galvanometer, the needle stays at the zero mark at the middle when no current passes through it (Figure 5.12a). When a current passes through it, the needle gets deflected. Unlike an ammeter, current may be passed in either direction through the galvanometer. The needle is deflected towards the right or the left from its middle position, depending on the direction of the current.

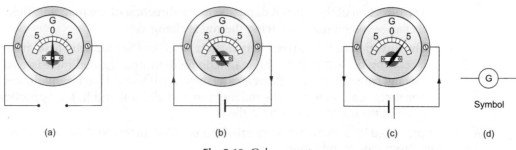

Fig. 5.12 Galvanometer

Connect the ends of a coil to a galvanometer. Since there is no current in the coil, the needle of the galvanometer will be at the zero mark. Now, bring a bar or rod magnet sharply towards the coil (Figure 5.13a). The galvanometer needle will get deflected in a particular direction (Figure 5.13b). When the magnet comes to rest, the needle comes back to its zero position, showing that the current in the coil has stopped. Now, move the magnet away from the coil. The needle will get deflected again, but this time, in the opposite direction (Figure 5.13c). This shows that the direction of the current has reversed. You will also find that the direction of the current depends on the pole of the magnet facing the coil while the magnet is moving.

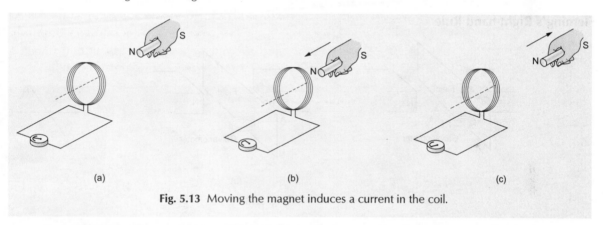

(a)   (b)   (c)

Fig. 5.13 Moving the magnet induces a current in the coil.

What happens if we move the coil instead of the magnet? Fix the coil to a wooden block, and move it sharply towards the magnet. You will find that as long as the coil moves, there is a current in the coil, as indicated by the deflection of the needle of the galvanometer (Figure 5.14a). And if you move the coil away from the magnet, the needle of the galvanometer gets deflected in the opposite direction (Figure 5.14b). There is no deflection, i.e., no current, when both of them are at rest.

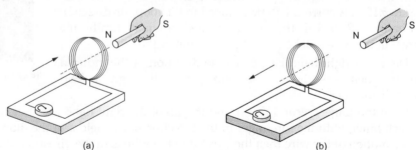

(a)   (b)

Fig. 5.14 Moving the coil near the magnet induces a current in it.

We conclude the following from the above activity.

(a) A current flows through a coil as long as a magnet moves near the coil, the coil moves near the magnet or both of them move. So, a current flows in the coil when there is relative motion between the magnet and the coil.

(b) While there is relative motion between the magnet and the coil, the magnetic field around the coil keeps changing. The changing magnetic field causes a current in the coil.

(c) The direction of the current depends on the direction of the magnetic field. That is why it changes when the pole facing the coil is changed.

(d) The direction of the current depends on whether the magnetic field around the coil is increasing or decreasing. The magnetic field around the coil increases as the coil and magnet come closer, and decreases as they move apart. That is why the current flows in one direction on moving the magnet towards the coil and in the opposite direction on moving the magnet away from the coil.

A current produced by a changing magnetic field is called an induced current. This phenomenon is called electromagnetic induction.

➤ **Electromagnetic Induction**	*The phenomenon in which an electric current is induced in a circuit because of a changing magnetic field is called electromagnetic induction.*

Electromagnetic induction was discovered by Michael Faraday in 1831. This important discovery revealed another link between electricity and magnetism. Not only can we use an electric current to produce a magnetic field, we can also use a magnetic field to produce an electric current.

Fleming's Right-hand Rule

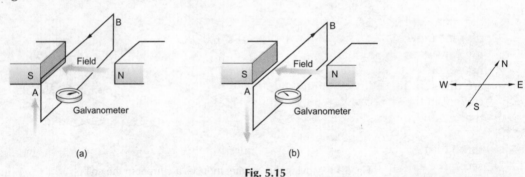

(a)   (b)

Fig. 5.15

Figure 5.15 shows a wire loop, a section *AB* of which lies in a magnetic field. A galvanometer is connected in the loop to detect current. In the figure, the magnetic field is from east to west, and the wire *AB* is perpendicular to this field, i.e., it lies in the south–north direction. Suppose the loop is pulled up vertically (Figure 5.15a). A current will be induced in the loop. Its direction will be from *B* to *A*. If the loop is pushed down vertically, the current in the wire will be from *A* to *B* (Figure 5.15b).

Fleming's right-hand rule gives the direction of the induced current when a section of a loop passes through a field perpendicular to it.

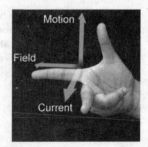

Fig. 5.16 Fleming's right-hand rule

If the forefinger, second finger and thumb of the right hand are stretched at right angles to each other, with the forefinger in the direction of the field and the thumb in the direction of the motion of the wire then the current in the wire is in the direction of the second finger.

Figure 5.16 illustrates the rule for the situation shown in Figure 5.15a. The forefinger and thumb are in the directions of the field and motion respectively. The stretched second finger gives the direction of the current. (Field is shown by the Forefinger, Current by the seCond finger, and Motion by the thuMb.)

Inducing Current without a Magnet

We have seen that the magnetic field of a permanent magnet can be used to induces a current in a wire. Can we induce a current using the magnetic field produced by another current? Yes, we can. The following activity will show you how.

Take a long nail and wind two coils side by side over it, as shown in Figure 5.17. The coils should have about 100 turns of thick enamelled copper wire. Connect one coil to a battery through a switch. This coil is called the first coil or the primary coil. Connect the other coil to a galvanometer or galvanoscope. This coil is called the second coil or the secondary coil.

Turn on the switch while looking at the galvanometer. You will see that the needle of the galvanometer gets deflected and then immediately returns to the zero mark, even while the switch is on. Now, turn off the switch. This time, the needle will get deflected in the opposite direction and then it will immediately return to the zero mark. The deflections in the galvanometer show that a current flows for a short while through the secondary.

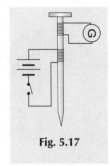

Fig. 5.17

When a current passes through the primary coil wrapped over the nail, a magnetic field is produced. This magnetic field changes when the switch is turned on or off. When you turn on the switch, the current in the primary *increases* from zero to some value in a very short time. And when you turn off the switch, the current in the primary *decreases* to zero in a very short time. A change (increase or decrease) in the current through the primary changes the magnetic field. The changing magnetic field induces a current in the secondary.

MOTOR AND GENERATOR

Many electrical devices are based on the relationship between electricity and magnetism. Two of the most important ones are the electric motor and the electric generator. Fans, mixies, CD players, motorized toys, etc., use motors. Motors are of different types. Some, like the motor in a toy car, work only on batteries, while others, like the motor of an electric pump, work on the household electric supply. Actually, the currents drawn from a battery and the household supply are different in nature. When an electrical device such as a bulb is connected to a battery, the current in the circuit always flows from the positive terminal (higher potential) of the battery to the negative terminal (lower potential). A current that always flows in the same direction through an electrical device is called a direct current (DC). However, the direction of the current flowing through the bulb of a reading lamp connected to the household supply changes rapidly every second. Such a current is called an alternating current (AC).

Electric motors and generators that work on DC or AC are only slightly different in construction. The principles of physics involved in both are the same. The fact that a current-carrying conductor experiences a force in a magnetic field is used in the electric motor. And, the fact that a changing magnetic field induces a current in a conductor is used in an electric generator. In an electric motor, electrical energy is converted into mechanical (kinetic) energy. On the other hand, a generator converts kinetic energy into electrical energy.

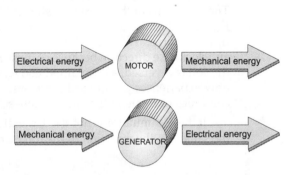

Fig. 5.18 Energy conversions in motors and generators

DC Motor

An electric motor is a device which uses electricity to rotate a rod, known as the shaft. The rotation of the shaft can be used to rotate anything (e.g., a wheel, the blades of a fan, etc.) attached to it. The basic design and working of a DC electric motor are described below.

Construction of a DC motor

The design of an electric motor is shown in Figure 5.19a. A motor basically consists of a coil placed in a magnetic field. The coil is formed by winding many turns of insulated copper wire over a soft iron core. The core and the coil together form the armature. The armature is fixed on the shaft of the motor and kept between the poles of a strong magnet. The two free ends of the coil

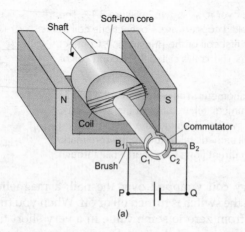

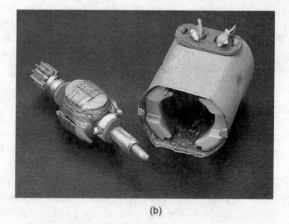

Fig. 5.19 (a) Schematic representation of a DC motor (b) You can see the essential parts if you open a motor used in a toy.

are connected to the two halves of a metallic split ring (a ring split in two separate parts). The split ring forms what is called the split-ring commutator or simply, commutator. When the shaft rotates, the commutator and the coil rotate with it. Two carbon brushes, B_1 and B_2, press against the two halves, C_1 and C_2, of the commutator. A potential difference is applied across the brushes by connecting them to a source of DC, for example, a battery.

Working of a DC motor

Look at Figure 5.20a. The brush B_1 is connected to the positive terminal of the battery, and B_2 is connected to the negative terminal. So, a current flows in the coil along $ABCD$ ($A \rightarrow B \rightarrow C \rightarrow D$). Figure 5.20b shows the position of the coil after half a rotation from the initial position. As a result of the rotation, the brushes with which the two halves of the commutator were in contact have got interchanged. This has reversed the battery connections to the two arms of the coil. Therefore, the current now flows along $DCBA$. That is, the direction of the current in the two arms of the coil has got reversed. Such a change takes place for each half-rotation. In this way, the commutator changes the direction of the current in the coil after each half-rotation.

The two arms of the coil carry a current in a magnetic field. So, each arm experiences a force. The directions of the forces are shown by the grey arrows in the figure. In the position shown in Figure 5.20a, the arm AB experiences a downward force, while the arm CD experiences an upward force. This may be verified using Fleming's left-hand rule. The coil rotates in the anticlockwise direction because of these forces. After half a rotation, the direction of the current in the coil is reversed, as explained above. Using Fleming's left-hand rule, we find that the arm AB now experiences an upward force, and the arm CD experiences a downward force. So, the coil continues to rotate in the anticlockwise direction.

If the commutator is not used, the direction of current in an arm of the coil will always remain the same. So, the direction of the force on the arm will not change, and the coil will not be able to

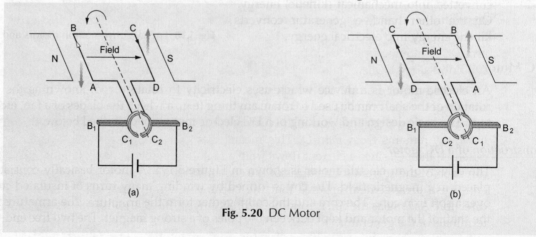

Fig. 5.20 DC Motor

complete one rotation. For example, when the arm *AB* is near the north pole, the downward force will turn it anticlockwise. And when it is near the south pole, the downward force will swing it back, clockwise. Thus, the rotation will not be completed.

DC Generator

When a conducting loop is rotated in a magnetic field, an electric current is induced in the loop. This fact is used in an electric generator, in which a coil is rotated in a magnetic field to produce electricity. Here, we shall learn about a DC generator, which is also called a dynamo.

Construction of a DC generator

Figure 5.21 shows the basic design of a DC generator, which is very similar to that of a DC motor. The armature of the generator consists of a coil of many turns wound over a soft iron core. The armature is placed between the poles of a strong magnet. The ends of the coil are connected to a split-ring commutator. Two carbon brushes, B_1 and B_2, press tightly against the two halves of the commutator. The brushes are connected to the fixed terminals, *P* and *Q*, of the generator. Electric devices such as an electric bulb can be connected to these terminals, as shown in the figure.

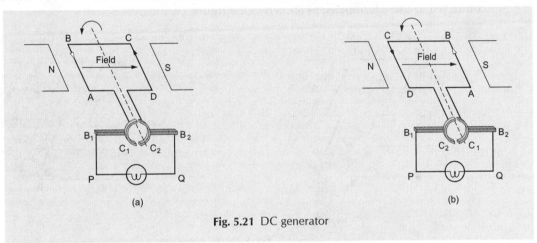

Fig. 5.21 DC generator

Working of a DC generator

To generate electricity, the shaft, on which the coil is mounted, needs to be rotated. In gensets, this is done by a small diesel engine. In the case of the dynamo of a bicycle, the rotating wheel rotates the shaft. In power stations, steam, water or wind falling on the blades of a turbine rotates the generator's shaft. As the coil rotates in the magnetic field, electricity is generated. When an electrical device is connected across the terminals of the generator, the circuit is completed and a current flows through the coil. If the terminals are left open, there is no current, but a potential difference appears between them.

In Figure 5.21a, the brushes B_1 and B_2 are in contact with the halves C_1 and C_2 of the commutator respectively. B_1 is connected to the terminal *P*, and B_2 is connected to the terminal *Q*. In the situation shown in Figure 5.21a, the arm *AB* of the coil is moving downwards, while the arm *DC* is moving upwards. Applying Fleming's left-hand rule, we find that the current in the coil flows along *DCBA*. Thus, the current flows through the bulb from *P* to *Q*.

After half a rotation, the brushes with which the two halves of the commutator were in contact get interchanged (Figure 5.21b). Now, the arm *AB* is moving upwards and the arm *DC* is moving downwards. This causes the current to flow along *ABCD*. The current through the bulb, however, remains from *P* to *Q*. This means that the terminal *P* always remains at a higher potential than *Q*, since a current flows from a higher to a lower potential. Note that although the direction of the current in the arms of the coil changes with each half-rotation, the commutator-and-brush arrangement ensures that the current in the external circuit remains in the same direction. As long as the coil is rotating, a direct current flows through the device connected to the terminals of the generator.

AC Generator

Suppose we remove the commutator from a DC generator, and make an arrangement so that the arm AB of the coil is always in electrical contact with the terminal P, and the arm CD is in contact with the terminal Q. Then with each half-rotation, as the direction of the current in the coil changes, the direction of the current in the bulb connected across the terminals of the generator also changes. An electric current that reverses its direction periodically is called an alternating current (AC). Most power-generating stations have AC generators. An AC generator is also called an alternator. It is similar in construction to a DC generator, with one major difference—the commutator is replaced by slip rings.

Construction of an AC generator

Figure 5.22 shows the basic design of an AC generator. The armature of the generator consists of a coil of many turns wound over a soft iron core. The armature is placed between the poles of a strong magnet. The ends of the coil are connected to two cylindrical slip rings, C_1 and C_2, mounted on the shaft. Each slip ring is permanently in contact with a carbon brush. The brushes are connected to the fixed terminals, P and Q. Electric devices such as an electric bulb can be connected to these terminals, as shown in the figure.

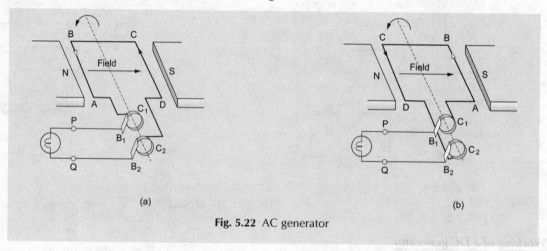

(a)

(b)

Fig. 5.22 AC generator

Working of an AC generator

To generate electricity, the shaft, on which the coil is mounted, is rotated. In Figure 5.22a, the arm AB of the coil is moving down, while the arm DC is moving up. Fleming's right-hand rule will show that the current in the coil is along $DCBA$. From A, the current flows to D via C_1, B_1, P, Q, B_2 and C_2. So, the current through the bulb is from P to Q.

Figure 5.22b shows the situation after half a rotation. The arm AB is now moving up and the arm DC is moving down. This causes the current to flow along $ABCD$. From D, the current flows to A via C_2, B_2, Q, P, B_1 and C_1. So, the current through the bulb is from Q to A.

Thus, as the direction of the current in the arms of the coil changes with each half-rotation, the direction of the current through the bulb changes. In other words, an alternating current flows through the bulb.

DOMESTIC ELECTRIC CIRCUITS

We use different electrical appliances in our houses which work on the electricity supplied from a power distribution station. Electricity generated at a power plant is distributed to consumers from distribution stations. In most places in India, the household power supply is AC. The supply is at 220 V, 50 Hz. Let us see what this means.

Alternating Current

Suppose you connect a bulb to an AC source such as the AC supply of your house (Figure 5.23a). The potential difference $V_A - V_B$ across the bulb keeps changing with time. When the current

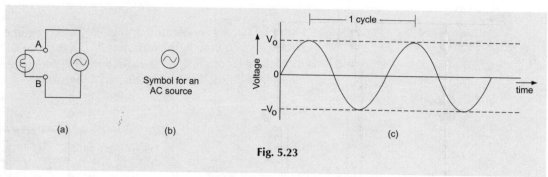

Fig. 5.23

flows from A to B in the bulb, $V_A > V_B$. When the current flows from B to A in the bulb, $V_A < V_B$. When the current becomes momentarily zero before changing direction, $V_A = V_B$. In fact, the potential difference across the bulb changes gradually from a maximum value V_o to zero and then to the minimum value $-V_o$. From $-V_o$, it increases to zero before reaching V_o once again. The way the potential difference (voltage) across the bulb changes with time is shown in Figure 5.23c. A plot of the alternating current through the bulb will also be similar. Starting from a particular value (say, maximum or minimum), when the current or voltage reaches that value next, it is said to complete one cycle. If it completes 1 cycle in one second, we say that its frequency is 1 hertz (Hz). The frequency of our household AC supply is 50 Hz, i.e., there are 50 cycles per second. This means it changes direction 100 times in 1 second.

Since the value of the AC voltage across a device such as a heater or a bulb does not remain constant, what is the effect on the amount of heat produced? It turns out that the heating effect of an AC voltage, whose peak value is V_o, is the same as that produced by a constant voltage of $V_o/\sqrt{2}$. This value is called its RMS voltage. When we say that the AC supply is at 220 V, we mean its RMS voltage is 220 V. The peak value of such a supply would be $\sqrt{2} \times (220 \text{ V}) = 310$ V.

Live, Neutral and Earth Wires

The electric power lines enter our house through three wires—the *live* wire, the neutral wire and the earth wire. What are these? The live wire is at 220 volts. The ground wire is maintained at zero potential by connecting it to a large plate buried in the ground. And the neutral wire is also maintained at almost zero potential. Current enters an appliance through the live wire and returns through the neutral wire. An appliance that consumes relatively low power, e.g., a tube light or a fan, has just two terminals. Using them, the appliance is connected across the live and neutral wires. Appliances such as heaters, electric irons, refrigerators, etc., have a third terminal, called the earth terminal. This terminal is connected to the metallic body of the appliance. The earth wire of the electric supply is connected to this terminal. This ensures that the metallic body is always at ground potential (0 V). The earth wire does not normally carry a current.

In two-terminal devices such as a bulb, it does not matter which terminal is connected to the live wire and which, to the neutral. But in an appliance such as an iron, if the live wire gets connected to the ground terminal, the body will be at 220 V. Anybody touching the body would get an electric shock. To prevent incorrect connections, the colour of the insulation of a wire is used to identify the type of wire. By convention, red is for live, black is for neutral and green is for earth. In the plug of a heater or a toaster, you will find wires of these colours connected to the terminals of the pins marked L, N and E.

All electrical appliances are connected across the neutral and live wires. The same potential difference is therefore, applied to all of them, and hence, they get connected in parallel to the power source. For each electric appliance and electrical socket connected to household wiring,

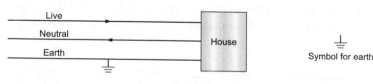

Fig. 5.24

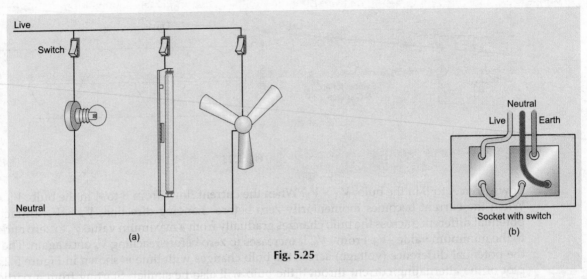

Fig. 5.25

there is a switch. Switches are always connected to the live wires. Figure 5.25a shows how the wiring of a room might look. In a socket-and-switch set, the live terminal of the socket gets connected to the live wire only when the switch is turned on. For this, the connections are made as shown in Figure 5.25b.

5-A and 15-A wirings

Different appliances have different resistances, and they draw different amounts of current when the same voltage is applied across them. A 2000-W heater has a resistance of about 25 Ω, whereas a 100-W bulb has a resistance of about 500 Ω. From Ohm's law, when 220 V is applied across each of them, the currents drawn by them are

$$I_{heater} = \frac{220\,V}{25\,\Omega} = 9\,A \qquad\qquad I_{bulb} = \frac{220\,V}{500\,\Omega} = 0.44\,A.$$

To carry larger currents, we need thicker wires and better-quality materials in electrical fittings such as switches and sockets. Two types of electrical fittings are usually available in the market—one meant for a maximum current of 5 A and the other for a maximum current of 15 A. Separate wires are drawn for 5-A and 15-A fittings, which are usually fixed on separate boards. The wires leading up to 15-A fittings are thicker than those leading up to 5-A fittings. Appliances that draw heavy currents are connected to the 15-A boards and the others, to the 5-A boards.

Electrical Problems and Safety Measures

Electric wires become heated when current passes through them. If, due to some reason, excessive heating takes place, the wires may catch fire. A fault like a short circuit or an overload can cause overheating of the wires.

Overload

Different types of wires can safely carry currents up to a certain limit, say 10 A or 20 A, before they start overheating. If the total current drawn through a wire by the appliances connected to it exceeds the safety limit for that wire, it gets overheated. We say that the overheating is due to overloading. For example, suppose a live wire entering the switchboard of a room can carry a maximum current of 10 A without overheating. The board has several switches for the fans and lights in the room, and it has a few sockets too. If we switch on all these appliances, and a heater, a toaster and an iron are connected to the sockets, the total current through the live wire entering the board will exceed 10 A. The overloaded wire will then get overheated.

Short circuit

Consider the situation shown in Figure 5.26a. A bulb is connected across the live and the neutral wires of the domestic supply. The current flowing through the circuit depends on the resistance of the bulb. Now consider the situation shown in Figure 5.26b, in which the live and the neutral

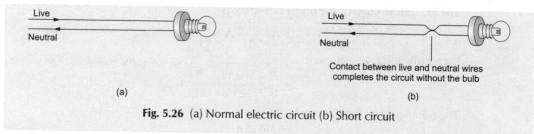

Fig. 5.26 (a) Normal electric circuit (b) Short circuit

wires have come in contact accidentally. A very large current passes through the circuit, because the resistance between the wires is now almost zero. Such an event is called a short circuit. The large current due to the short circuit leads to overheating, which may even cause a fire. A short circuit may happen due to many reasons, including the insulations on neighbouring wires getting worn out, a conductor such as a screw falling across the live and the neutral terminals of a socket, and so on.

Safety devices

To prevent accidents, safety devices are used in circuits involving high voltages (normally, 100 V or more). These safety devices break the circuit whenever an abnormally high current flows through it. Common safety devices include the fuse and the circuit breaker. You already know how a fuse works. The fuse wire melts when the current through it exceeds its rated value. This breaks the circuit. Let us see how a circuit breaker works.

A circuit breaker has a switch and a solenoid connected in series in the live line of a circuit. A heavy soft iron core lies partially in the solenoid. When a current greater than a particular value passes through the solenoid, the core gets pulled in. The core hits the switch to open it and break the circuit. The switch can be turned on again manually once the electrical fault is rectified. Figure 5.27 shows how a circuit breaker works.

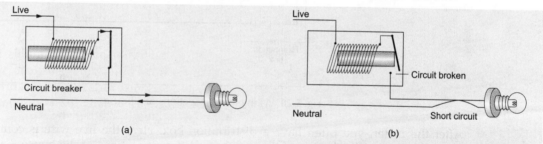

Fig. 5.27 (a) Under normal circumstances, the core of the circuit breaker lies partially inside the solenoid. (b) A current greater than a particular value flowing through the solenoid pulls in the core, which opens the switch.

EXAMPLE 5.1 The mains power supply of a house is through a 5-A fuse. How many 100-W bulbs can be used in this house at the correct voltage?

Solution The current in each bulb is

$$i = \frac{P}{V} = \frac{100 \text{ W}}{220 \text{ V}} = \frac{5}{11} \text{ A}.$$

For the current through the fuse to be 5 A, the number of bulbs

$$= \frac{5 \text{ A}}{\frac{5}{11} \text{ A}} = 11.$$

EXAMPLE 5.2 Electric supply of a house is through a 15-A fuse. When a 2000-W heater is used in this house, how many 100-W bulbs can be used simultaneously? The supply is at 220 V, and the heater and the bulbs are rated for 220 V.

Solution The current drawn by the 2000-W heater is

$$i = \frac{P}{V} = \frac{2000 \text{ W}}{220 \text{ V}} = \frac{100}{11} \text{ A}.$$

The maximum current the bulbs can draw is

$$15 \text{ A} - \frac{100}{11} \text{ A} = \frac{65}{11} \text{ A}.$$

Each bulb will take a current

$$i = \frac{P}{V} = \frac{100 \text{ W}}{220 \text{ V}} = \frac{5}{11} \text{ A}.$$

The number of bulbs that can be used is

$$\frac{65/11 \text{ A}}{5/11 \text{ A}} = 13.$$

Domestic Wiring

The wiring inside a house is done according to the needs of its different areas. The electric wires entering the house go through a meter board. Here the live wire goes through a main fuse (or circuit breaker) and a meter that records the electric power consumed. Electricity bills are paid based on the readings of this meter. Removing the main fuse from its socket cuts the supply to the whole house. The main fuse blows when the sum of currents being drawn by the different circuits in the house exceeds a limit.

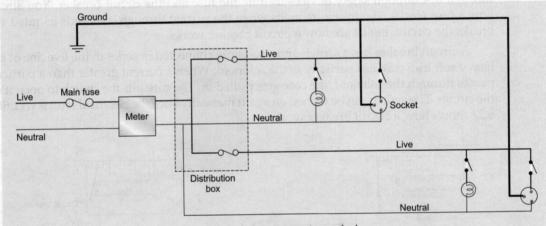

Fig. 5.28 Wiring for two sections of a house

After the meter, you often have a distribution box. Here the live wire is connected to a number of wires for distribution of the supply to different sections of the house. Each of these wires thus becomes live. A fuse is connected to each of them. The live wires go to different sections of the house. This distribution method has an advantage. If there is an electrical fault in one section of the house, only the fuse connected to its live wire blows. The supply to the rest of the house remains unaffected.

Earthing of electric appliances

Usually, electric appliances with high power rating such as heaters, irons, etc., have a terminal for connecting the earth wire, in addition to terminals for the live and neutral wires. The earth wire is

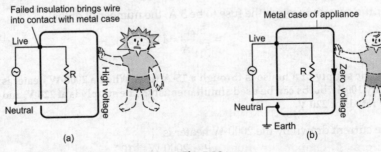

Fig. 5.29

connected to the metallic body of the appliance. This is done to avoid shocks in case of a fault. Suppose, due to some reason, the insulation of the live wire inside an electric iron gets burnt at a place. If the metallic body of the iron is in contact with the defective wire, it will be at a potential of 220 V when the iron is in use. If a person accidentally touches the metallic body of the iron, he/she will get an electric shock. However, with the earth, wire properly connected to the metallic body, the current will quickly go to the earth, and the potential of the metallic body will not rise. Thus, earthing of electric appliances protects us from electric shocks.

· POINTS TO REMEMBER ·

- *Magnetic field*

    A magnet produces a magnetic field in the space around it, which exerts a force on any other magnet placed in it. Each point in this field has a particular strength and direction. The direction of the magnetic field can be found by placing a magnetic compass at that point. The needle of the compass settles along the direction of the field.

- *Magnetic field lines*

    A line such that the tangent at any point on it gives the direction of the magnetic field at that point is called a magnetic field line or magnetic line of force.

- *Magnetic field due to a straight current-carrying conductor*

    An electric current produces a magnetic field. The magnetic field lines due to a straight current-carrying conductor are circular, with their centres on the wire. The direction of this field can be found by Maxwell's right-hand thumb rule, which states that *if a straight current-carrying wire is imagined to be held in the right hand, with the thumb stretched along the direction of the current, the direction of the magnetic field produced by the current is in the direction in which the fingers are curled.*

- *Magnetic field due to currents in coils and solenoids*

    The direction of the magnetic field at a point on the axis of a current-carrying circular coil or a loop a can be found from the following rule. *If the fingers of the right hand are curled along the direction of the current in a loop, the stretched thumb gives the direction of the magnetic field.* At other points, the direction may be different.

    The magnetic field inside a current-carrying solenoid is nearly uniform and is parallel to the axis. The field outside the solenoid is similar to that produced by a bar magnet. If you hold the solenoid in your right hand, with fingers curled along the current, the thumb gives the direction of the field within it, as well as the direction in which the north pole of the solenoid appears.

- *Electromagnet*

    A magnet formed temporarily due to the magnetic field of a current is called an electromagnet. When an electric current is passed through a solenoid that has a core of a magnetic material like iron, the core becomes an electromagnet. The magnetism disappears when the current is stopped. The poles can be switched by reversing the direction of the current.

    The cores of electromagnets use soft magnetic materials like soft iron. This is to ensure that the electromagnet loses its magnetism once the current is switched off. Permanent magnets are made of hard magnetic materials like Alnico.

- *Force on a current-carrying wire by a magnetic field*

    When a current-carrying wire is placed in a magnetic field, a force acts on the wire. The direction of the force depends on the direction of the magnetic field as well as the direction of the current. The direction of the force is given by Fleming's left-hand rule: *If the forefinger, second finger and thumb of the left hand are stretched at right angles to each other, with the forefinger in the direction of the field and the second finger in the direction of the current then the thumb indicates the direction of the force.*

- *Electromagnetic induction*

    The phenomenon in which an electric current is induced in a circuit because of a changing magnetic field is called electromagnetic induction. For example, relative motion between a coil and a magnet induces a current in the coil whose direction is given by Fleming's right-hand rule: *If the forefinger, second finger and thumb of the right hand are stretched at right angles to each other, with the forefinger in the direction of the field and the thumb in the direction of the motion of the wire then the current in the wire is in the direction of the second finger.*

    (For both rules given by Fleming, Field corresponds to the Forefinger, Current to the seCond finger and Movement (or force) to the thuMb.)

- *DC and AC*

    A current that always flows in the same direction through an electrical device is called a direct current (DC). An electric current that reverses its direction periodically is called an alternating current (AC).

• *Electric motor*

An electric motor converts electrical energy into mechanical energy. The fact that a current-carrying conductor experiences a force in a magnetic field is used in an electric motor. In a DC motor, the current flowing in a coil kept between the poles of a magnet makes it turn. A commutator is used to change the direction of the current in the coil at each half-rotation to keep the coil turning.

• *Electric generator*

An electric generator converts kinetic energy into electrical energy. The fact that a changing magnetic field induces a current in a conductor is used in an electric generator. A coil kept between the poles of a magnet is rotated. The current induced in the coil changes direction after each half-rotation. In an AC generator, this alternating current passes through slip rings to the terminals of the generator. In a DC generator, the direction of the current flowing in the external circuit is kept the same by a commutator.

• *Domestic circuits*

In India, the household electric supply is AC 200 V, 50 Hz. All electrical appliances in the house are connected in parallel.

• *Electrical problems and safety measures*

When a wire carries more current than it can carry without overheating, it is said to be *overloaded*. An event in which a large current passes through the wires when the live and neutral wires touch accidentally is called a *short circuit*. An overload or a short circuit causes excessive heating of the wire, which may even cause a fire. To prevent this, fuses or circuit breakers are used.

To prevent electric shocks in the event of the live wire touching the metallic body of an appliance, the body is connected to the earth wire.

· EXERCISES ·

A. *Very-Short-Answer Questions*

1. How can you find the direction of a magnetic field at a point through which the magnetic line of force is given?

2. Sketch the shape of magnetic field lines near a straight wire carrying a current.

3. How will you show that the magnetic field produced by a current-carrying wire decreases with distance from the wire?   **(2006)**

4. How is the strength of the magnetic field at a point near a current-carrying wire related to the current?   **(2004)**

5. A circular wire is carrying a current. Sketch the shape of the magnetic field lines in a plane that is perpendicular to the plane of the wire and passes through its centre.

6. A circular loop carrying a current is placed on a horizontal surface. As seen from above, the current is in the clockwise direction. What is the direction of its magnetic field at the centre? What is the direction of the magnetic field at a point outside the surface of the loop?

7. A vertical wire is carrying a current in the upward direction. It is placed in a magnetic field pointing towards the east. Find the direction of the force on the wire.

8. A beam of electrons can be thought of as an electric current whose direction is opposite the direction of the moving electrons. Suppose you find that an electron beam coming towards you horizontally through a magnetic field gets deflected towards your right. What is the direction of the magnetic field that bends the beam?   [Ans: Upwards]

9. A wire loop is moved into a magnetic field. You have to find the direction of the current in a portion of the loop that is moving perpendicular to the field. Will you use Fleming's left-hand rule or right-hand rule?

10. An electric current is passed through a copper wire by connecting its ends to a battery. It is kept between the poles of a strong horseshoe magnet. There is a force on the wire due to the magnet. If you interchange the connections to the positive and negative terminals of the battery, and also the positions of the north and south poles of the magnet, what will be the change in the force on the wire due to the magnet?

11. What is the purpose of Fleming's right-hand rule?

12. A motor converts energy from one form to other. Name the two forms in sequence.

13. A generator converts energy from one form to other. Name the two forms in sequence.

14. Which wire (live, neutral or earth) goes through a switch?

15. Are different electric appliances connected in series or parallel in a house?

16. What is the colour convention for live, neutral and earth wires?

B. *Short-Answer Type Questions*

1. State Maxwell's right-hand thumb rule for finding the direction of the magnetic field due to a current-carrying straight wire.

2. Why does a compass needle get deflected when a magnet is brought near it? Explain in terms of the magnetic field.

3. Why cannot two magnetic field lines cut each other?

4. What is a solenoid? How is it different from a coil?

5. How is an electromagnet different from a permanent magnet?

6. Knowing the direction of the current, how will you determine the side on which the north pole is formed in an electromagnet?

7. Can a magnetic field be produced without using a magnet? If yes, how?

8. What is the use of the commutator in a DC motor?

9. State the principles (one sentence each) on which an electric motor and an electric generator are based.

10. What is the basic difference between an AC and a DC generator?

11. What is an overload in an electric circuit?

C. Long-Answer Questions

1. Describe an experiment to show that an electric current produces a magnetic field.

2. Describe an experiment to show that a magnetic field exerts a force on a current-carrying wire.

3. How will you show that the direction of the force exerted by a magnet on a current-carrying conductor depends on the directions of the magnetic field and the current?

4. You are given a strong bar magnet and a compass. Describe a method by which the magnetic field lines due to the bar magnet can be drawn.

5. What is an electromagnet? How can you make an electromagnet? **(2006)**

6. What is electromagnetic induction? Describe an experiment to demonstrate it.

7. What is induced current? Describe two ways of producing an induced current in a coil.

8. State Fleming's left-hand rule. Draw a neat diagram showing the different parts of a DC motor. Explain its working. **(2005)**

9. What is Fleming's right-hand rule? With a neat diagram explain the working of an AC generator. **(2005)**

10. What do you understand by live, neutral and earth wires? Do all the three normally carry electricity?

11. What is the function of the earth wire in electric lines? Why is the metallic body of an electric appliance connected to the earth wire?

12. What is a short circuit? How does a fuse help in case there is a short circuit?

13. An electric heater is rated 2 kW, 220 V. If a fuse is to be connected to it, should it be rated 5 A or 15 A?

D. Objective Questions

I. Pick the correct option.

1. A magnetic field line is used to find the direction of
   (a) south–north   (b) a bar magnet
   (c) a compass needle   (d) magnetic field

2. An electric current passes through a straight wire. Magnetic compasses are placed at the points A and B.

   (a) Their needles will not deflect.
   (b) Only one of the needles will deflect.
   (c) Both the needles will deflect in the same direction.
   (d) The needles will deflect in the opposite directions.

3. The magnetic field lines due to a straight wire carrying a current are
   (a) straight   (b) circular
   (c) parabolic   (d) elliptical

4. The magnetic field lines inside a long current-carrying solenoid are nearly
   (a) straight   (b) circular
   (c) parabolic   (d) elliptical

5. The direction of the force on a current-carrying wire placed in a magnetic field depends on
   (a) the direction of the current but not on the direction of the field
   (b) the direction of the field but not on the direction of the current
   (c) the direction of the current as well as the direction of the field
   (d) neither the direction of the current nor the direction of the field

6. An electric current can be produced in a closed loop
   (a) by connecting it to a battery, but not by moving a magnet near it
   (b) by moving a magnet near the loop, but not by connecting a battery
   (c) by connecting it to a battery, as well as by moving a magnet near it
   (d) neither by connecting a battery nor by moving a magnet near it

7. Which of the following involves electromagnetic induction?
   (a) A rod is charged with electricity.
   (b) An electric current produces a magnetic field.
   (c) A magnetic field exerts a force on a current-carrying wire.
   (d) The relative motion between a magnet and a coil produces an electric current.

8. You have a coil and a bar magnet. You can produce an electric current by moving
   (a) the magnet, but not the coil
   (b) the coil, but not the magnet
   (c) either the magnet or the coil
   (d) neither the magnet nor the coil

9. An electric motor
   (a) provides a constant potential difference
   (b) measures electric current
   (c) measures potential difference
   (d) converts electrical energy into kinetic energy

10. A device that can be used to produce an electric current in a circuit is
  (a) an ammeter (b) a motor
  (c) a generator (d) a galvanometer

11. A commutator changes the direction of current in the coil of
  (a) a DC motor
  (b) a DC motor and an AC generator
  (c) a DC motor and a DC generator
  (d) an AC generator

12. An AC generator is connected to an electric appliance. In 10 revolutions of the armature, the current in the appliance changes direction
  (a) 5 times (b) 10 times
  (c) 20 times (d) 40 times

13. Which of the following describes the common domestic power supplied in India?
  (a) 220 V, 100 Hz (b) 110 V, 100 Hz
  (c) 220 V, 50 Hz (d) 110 V, 50 Hz

14. In electric fittings in a house
  (a) the live wire goes through the switch
  (b) the neutral wire goes through the switch
  (c) the earth wire goes through the switch
  (d) no wire goes through the switch

15. An electric fuse is based on
  (a) the heating effect of the current
  (b) the chemical effect of the current
  (c) the magnetic effect of the current
  (d) none of these

16. An electric fuse can prevent accidents arising from
  (a) an overload but not due to a short circuit
  (b) a short circuit but not due to an overload
  (c) an overload as well as a short circuit
  (d) neither an overload nor a short circuit

II. *Mark the statements True (T) or False (F).*

1. Fleming's left-hand rule is used to find the direction of the magnetic field due to a straight current.

2. Maxwell's right-hand thumb rule is used to find the direction of the magnetic field due to a straight current.

3. The magnetic field at the centre of a current-carrying coil is perpendicular to the plane of the coil.

4. The magnetic field lines inside a current-carrying solenoid are circular.

5. A motor is used to generate electricity from the mechanical motion of a coil.

6. A generator is used to generate electricity from the mechanical motion of a coil.

7. When a coil is moved towards a bar magnet placed perpendicular to it, an electric current is induced in the coil.

8. A battery provides an AC voltage.

9. If a coil and a magnet are moved in the same direction and with the same speed, an electric current will be induced in the coil.

10. Two coils are kept near each other. If a constant current flows through one, a current will be induced in the other.

11. A fuse is connected in series with the circuit it protects.

12. The current through a short circuit is very high.

13. Fans, lamps, etc., are connected in parallel in household wiring.

14. The earth wire connected to an electric appliance does not carry an electric current unless a fault develops in the insulation of the wires.

III. *Fill in the blanks.*

1. The magnetic field lines near a current-carrying straight wire are ...... in shape.

2. In the statement of Fleming's left-hand rule, the forefinger represents the ...... , the middle finger represents the ...... and the thumb represents the ....

3. A current passes through a wire from south to north. The direction of the magnetic field at a point vertically above the wire will be from ...... to ....

4. A wire carries electric current from south to north. If it is placed in a magnetic field pointing towards the west, the force on it will be pointing towards the ....

5. When a magnet is brought towards a metallic loop, an electric current is produced in the loop. This is an example of electromagnetic ....

6. The ...... wire should first go to the switch and then to the appliance.

7. The colours recommended for wires carrying live, neutral and earth lines are ...... , ... and ...... respectively.

· ANSWERS ·

D. *Objective Questions*
I. 1. (d) 2. (d) 3. (b) 4. (a) 5. (c)
  6. (c) 7. (d) 8. (c) 9. (d) 10. (c)
  11. (a) 12. (c) 13. (c) 14. (a) 15. (a)
  16. (c)

II. 1. F 2. T 3. T 4. F 5. F
  6. T 7. T 8. F 9. F 10. F
  11. T 12. T 13. T 14. T

· POSTSCRIPT ·

How is magnetism produced?

We have studied in this chapter that an electric current produces a magnetic field. Is electric current the source of all magnetic fields? We know that a permanent magnet produces a magnetic field without any current being passed through it. You will be surprised to know that actually electric current is also behind the magnetism of permanent magnets. You know that the permanent magnet is made up of a large number of atoms, and that each atom contains electrons which are charged particles. A moving electron is equivalent to an electric current. In a permanent magnet, all these atomic currents cooperate with each other to produce strong magnetism.

Make a galvanoscope

An ammeter is used to measure an electric current. You can make a galvanoscope to detect currents and also to compare two currents.

Take a magnetic compass and wind about 40 turns of enamelled copper wire around it. Use tape to keep the turns in place, keeping the ends of the wire free (Figure 5.A1). The galvanoscope is ready. To test it, connect the free ends of the wire to the two terminals of a cell. You will see that the needle gets deflected. The deflection of the needle tells you that a current is passing through the wire. Test an old cell and a new cell, and note the deflections of the needle in each case. You will see that the deflection is more with the new cell and less with the old cell. This shows that with a new

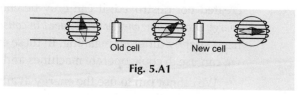

Fig. 5.A1

Sources of Energy

Energy, as you know, is the capacity to do work. You also know that in a given situation when all forms of energy are taken into account, the total energy remains constant. Energy can neither be created nor destroyed; it can only be changed from one form to another. Yet you hear about *energy production, energy crisis, need to conserve energy,* and so on. The term 'energy' used in these has a slightly different meaning. In these expressions, we refer to the energy in a useful form that we can use to cook, operate machines and appliances, run vehicles, and so on.

We cannot put to use the energy available from every source. We can only put to use energy from specific sources, which we call sources of energy. For example, the potential energy of a rock high up on a hill cannot be used to cook food, but the chemical energy in cooking gas (liquefied petroleum gas, LPG) can. So, the rock is not a source of energy, but LPG is. Some common sources of energy include firewood, coal, petroleum, natural gas, flowing water and uranium. We also use the energy of the sun and the wind. So, they are also energy sources.

Good Sources of Energy

What is a good source of energy? That depends on many things such as the purpose for which it is needed, available resources, etc. What is good for a village might not be suitable for a factory. For choosing a source of energy for a particular purpose, we evaluate the following characteristics.

Energy output per unit volume The energy output per unit volume (or mass) of a good source of energy should be high. The gas in a 15-kg LPG cylinder can be used by a family of average size to cook food for about a month. To cook the same amount of food using wood, you would need a roomful of wood. Clearly, the energy output per unit volume of LPG, which takes a small space in the kitchen, is much higher than that of wood.

Steady availability The energy source should be available readily and for a long time. For example, coal and petroleum have been readily available for a long time. Although the sun is a good source of energy, it is available only during the day. Similarly, wind energy is reliable only in those places where there is always a wind.

Safe and easy to use For widespread use, the source of energy has to be safe and easy to use. A fuel that produces a lot of smoke is not a good source of energy, since it is not safe for people's health. A nuclear power plant is not easy to build and operate. This limits the use of nuclear fuels like uranium.

Easy to store and transport Most common sources of energy such as coal, petrol and LPG need to be transported to users from their points of production. They also need to be stored before use. We should be able to transport and store such sources of energy safely and economically.

Economical The source of energy has to be economical. Hydrogen is an excellent fuel. But, it is not widely used as it is costly to produce, store and transport it.

Classification of Sources of Energy

We can classify energy sources in different ways. One classification is based on the reserves (supply) of an energy source. Another is based on how long we have been using it.

Renewable and nonrenewable sources of energy

We have vast but fixed reserves of coal, natural gas and petroleum. These were formed by natural processes over millions of years. However, the rate at which we have been using these sources, their reserves will not last very long. Unfortunately, we cannot regenerate them. On the other hand, the sun will continue to shine for about another 4.5 billion years. So, as long as there is life on earth, we can use solar energy. Sources of energy can be called renewable or nonrenewable based on their reserves as well as our ability to generate them.

Renewable sources of energy are those which can be generated by us or which are constantly being generated by natural processes or whose supply is unlimited.

Nonrenewable sources of energy are those which were produced in the past by natural processes, whose supply is limited and which we cannot generate ourselves.

Coal, natural gas and petroleum are nonrenewable sources of energy. Wood is a renewable source of energy although its supply is limited. But, if we replant and use trees in a planned manner, we can be assured of a continuous supply of firewood. The sun, wind and flowing water are also renewable sources because of their unlimited availability. Unlike fuels like coal, nuclear fuels such as uranium are required in very small quantities to generate electricity. So, their reserves will last for a long, long time. They are therefore classified as renewable sources of energy.

Conventional and nonconventional sources of energy

Sources of energy that have been in use for centuries are called conventional sources of energy. Conventional sources include wood, coal, petroleum and flowing water. Conventional sources like coal and petroleum are nonrenewable, while sources like flowing water are renewable.

Sources of energy that we have started using in new ways or only in recent times are called nonconventional or alternate sources of energy. These include energy from the sun, the heat inside the earth (geothermal energy), tides, ocean waves, etc. Nuclear energy is also a nonconventional source. Note that nonconventional energy sources are renewable. Our government has started giving great attention to these sources.

We have been using wind and biomass (like cow dung) for energy for ages. In that sense they are conventional sources. However, they were not used conventionally to do tasks like electricity generation, which has now been made possible with improvement in technology. In that sense they can also be called nonconventional sources of energy.

FOSSIL FUELS

Fuels that were formed from the remains of dead plants and animals are called fossil fuels. These were produced by complex processes with the help of a series of natural events over millions of years. The most widely used fossil fuels are coal, petroleum and natural gas. You know that plants trap solar energy in the form of food, and animals get energy when they eat the plants. *Since fossil fuels came from plants and animals, their ultimate source of energy is the sun.*

We get a number of different fuels from coal and petroleum. For example, we get petrol, diesel, kerosene and LPG from petroleum, and coke and natural gas from coal. When burnt in air, fossil fuels give off heat, which is used for various purposes—from cooking to generating electricity. However, these fuels are nonrenewable, and their reserves are running out. Unfortunately, we cannot repeat the events that led to their formation.

Fossil fuels have played an important role in the technological advances made in the last three hundred years or so. Even today, most of the energy requirements of homes, industries and transport are met by fossil fuels. It is estimated that about 25% of our total energy consumption comes from coal. More than 90% of this coal is used for electricity generation in thermal power plants.

In most thermal power plants, coal is burnt to heat water for producing steam. The steam falls on the blades of a special kind of wheel called a turbine. A turbine is a device that rotates when steam, water or wind falls on its blades. The turbine turns the shaft of an electric generator to which it is connected. In this way electricity is produced.

Cut small rectangular strips from a can to make the blades of a turbine. Make cuts on the edge of a round plastic lid (cover) and fix the blades in them with glue, as shown. Fix a small length of tube (from the refill of a pen) at the centre of the lid. Slide its free end over the shaft of a motor from a toy. If you blow on the blades of your turbine, it will rotate, and so will the shaft of the motor. The turbine will also rotate when steam from a kettle or a jet of water falls on its blades.

Since DC motors and generators are similar in construction, your motor acts as a generator when its shaft is rotated. You will detect a current by connecting its wires to a sensitive galvanoscope or milliammeter. With a powerful motor, you may be able to light an LED.

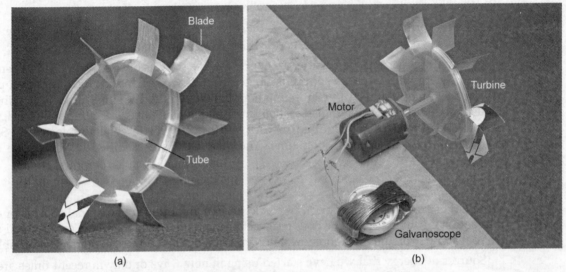

Fig. 6.1 (a) Homemade turbine (b) The turbine connected to a motor

Thermal power plants generated 65.6% of the total electricity produced in India in 2006. The rest was generated by hydroelectric (26.6%), nuclear (3%) and renewable-energy (4.8%) power plants.

In some thermal power plants, natural gas or oil is used as fuel. Natural gas is mainly methane (CH_4). *It is the cleanest fossil fuel, producing lesser pollutants than other fossil fuels.* That is why vehicles using compressed natural gas (CNG) cause less pollution.

Pollution Caused by Burning Fossil Fuels

The burning of most fossil fuels causes air pollution. The pollutants produced include carbon dioxide, carbon monoxide, oxides of nitrogen, sulphur dioxide and unburnt particles.

(a) Burning of fossil fuels like coal and petrol produces carbon dioxide. Excess carbon dioxide in the atmosphere is increasing the greenhouse effect, leading to unnatural global warming.

(b) When coal and petrol do not burn completely, carbon monoxide is produced. Excessive inhalation of this poisonous gas can cause death.

(c) During the combustion of coal, sulphur present in it forms sulphur dioxide. Oxides of nitrogen are formed when atmospheric nitrogen and oxygen combine at the high temperatures inside a running automobile engine. In the air, sulphur dioxide combines with oxygen and water to form sulphuric acid. Oxides of nitrogen form nitric acid. These fall on the earth with rain, which we call acid rain. Acid rain damages soil, water bodies, crops, living tissues and structures like the Taj Mahal.

(d) The unburnt particles produced during the combustion of fossil fuels are carried by smoke. They affect our lungs, and blacken clothes and buildings. The pollution caused by burning coal can be greatly reduced by installing a tall chimney or by installing a precipitator, which is a device that reduces the amount of suspended matter in the smoke.

ENERGY FROM FLOWING WATER: HYDRO ENERGY

When we talk of flowing water, we think of water flowing in rivers, streams, waterfalls, and so on. The flowing water has kinetic energy. The ultimate source of this energy is the sun. This is because the energy of the sun evaporates water, which forms clouds that cause rainfall or snowfall. The rain and melting snow feed rivers, etc., whose flow we use.

The energy of flowing water has been used for centuries to carry logs down rivers, to turn waterwheels to grind grain, run mills, and so on. Water striking the blades of the waterwheel makes it rotate. This design was modified to make water turbines, which are used to generate electricity from flowing water.

Fig. 6.2 Waterwheel

Hydroelectricity

Electricity generated by using the kinetic energy of flowing water is called hydroelectricity. The electric power thus generated is called hydroelectric power.

Electricity is generated from flowing water at a hydroelectric power plant. For large hydroelectric plants, water from a river is diverted to a large reservoir, which is an artificial lake to store water. A high dam is constructed on one side of the reservoir to hold back the water. The building housing the generator is at the base of the dam, on its other side. Water flows down through pipes from near the top of the dam to the generator house below. It strikes the blades of a water turbine with tremendous speed, making it rotate. The turbine rotates the shaft of a generator to which it is connected. This makes the generator produce electricity. In this way, the kinetic energy of flowing water is used to rotate the turbine, and the rotational kinetic energy is converted into electrical energy.

It is not necessary to set up large dams for hydroelectric plants. Small hydroelectric plants can be set up to generate electricity from a few hundred kilowatts to tens of megawatts. Such plants can use water diverted from a waterfall or from a dam built for irrigation.

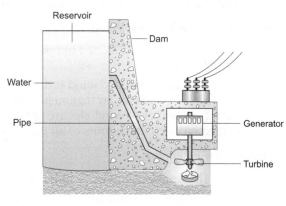

(a)　　　(b)

Fig. 6.3 (a) Dam and reservoir (b) Diagram of a hydroelectric power plant

Advantages of hydroelectricity

(a) The source of energy (water) is free and renewable.

(b) Harnessing the energy of flowing water is a pollution-free process, with no smoke, chemicals, etc., being produced.

(c) The cost of electricity generation is low as compared to electricity generated from other types of power plants.

(d) Flowing water is a more reliable source of energy than wind.

(e) Hydroelectricity can be generated on a large scale from a single plant.

(f) Dams built for hydroelectric plants also help in flood control and irrigation.

(g) Small hydroelectric stations are one of the best options for generating electricity from renewable sources, as they do not affect the environment much.

Disadvantages of hydroelectricity

(a) Dams built for large hydroelectric plants submerge a large area of land under water. This affects the plants and animals of the region. People of the area lose their lands. Apart from this, blocking or changing the course of a river affects fish and other organisms of the river.

(b) Large hydroelectric power plants are expensive to build.

(c) Not all rivers and not all areas are suitable for hydroelectric power generation.

Scope of hydroelectricity

Hydroelectricity has huge potential worldwide. In India, it is estimated that 145,000 MW of hydroelectricity can be generated. Out of this, by 2006, India had an installed capacity of about 34,000 MW.

WIND ENERGY

A moving mass of air is called wind. Let us see, with the help of an example, what causes wind. During the day, the land near the sea heats up faster than the water of the sea. Therefore, the air over the land heats up faster than that over the sea. The warm air over the land rises, and to take its place the colder air from the sea moves towards the land. This moving air is called wind. Similarly, winds arise whenever two adjoining areas on the surface of the earth are unequally heated by the sun. Like any moving object, wind has kinetic energy. Clearly, the ultimate source of this energy is the sun.

The invention of the windmill made it possible to do things like grind grain at mills and lift water with the help of wind energy. A windmill is a device in which the energy of the wind is used to rotate a set of blades, and the rational energy of the blades is used to do some work. The blades of a modern windmill make it look like a fan mounted on a tall column. The blades are kept high above the ground to catch the wind.

Generating Electricity from Wind

A windmill can be designed to rotate the shaft of a generator. Such a windmill is usually called a wind turbine.

A specially designed wind turbine is connected to the shaft of small generator. The electricity produced by such an arrangement is not sufficient even for a small town. To be commercially useful, a number of wind-electric generators are set up in a large area, called a wind farm. The combined electrical outputs of all the generators are then used to supply power.

Advantages of wind energy

(a) The source of energy (wind) is free.

(b) Harnessing wind energy is a pollution-free process, with no smoke, chemicals, etc., being produced.

(c) A small wind-electric plant can be set up near a factory to provide pollution-free power for its use.

Limitations of wind energy

(a) Wind energy cannot be harnessed at places where wind does not blow regularly. A wind-electric generator works only on winds of at least 15 km/h.

(b) Wind is not a dependable source of energy because sometimes the air is absolutely still and at other times there are storms.

(c) It is expensive to set up a wind farm for generating electricity because wind farms need a large area.

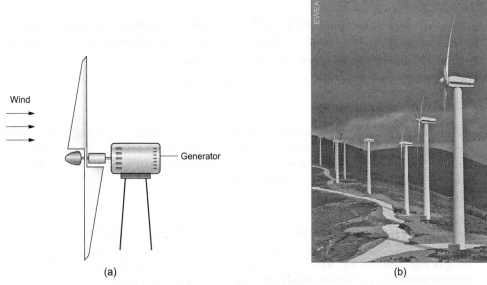

Fig 6.4 (a) Wind turbine (b) Wind farm

Scope of wind energy

It is estimated that India can produce more than 45,000 MW of electricity from wind energy. By 2005, India had an installed wind-electric capacity of about 2500 MW. This made India among the top five producers of electricity from wind along with Germany, USA, Denmark and Spain. The state leading in wind-electric generation was Tamil Nadu.

ENERGY FROM BIOMASS

What is biomass? In the context of energy production, biomass is any organic matter from which we can get energy on a renewable basis. It includes agricultural residues, wood, animal excreta, wastes from food processing and municipal wastes. Agricultural residues include straw, hay and husk. Waste from food processing includes bagasse, which is the residue left after extracting the juice from sugar cane. Cow dung (*gobar*) has been a traditional biomass fuel in our country. Since plants trap solar energy in the form of food, and animals eat plants, the ultimate source of biomass energy is the sun

Fig. 6.5 A traditional *chulha*

Wood

Wood has been a major source of energy since man discovered fire. It is still used widely as a fuel for cooking and heating. In many Indian homes, food is cooked on stoves that use biomass fuels such as wood. Such a stove is called a *chulha*.

A traditional chulha operates at a very low efficiency. Hardly 10% of the energy contained in the wood is utilized. Also, it does not burn the wood completely, which causes a lot of smoke. Indian scientists have designed several 'smokeless' chulhas. These produce much less smoke, and the fuel is more efficiently utilized.

Wood can be more efficiently utilized by converting it into charcoal. Charcoal is prepared by burning wood in an insufficient supply of oxygen. The process of burning wood in insufficient supply of oxygen is called destructive distillation of wood. Wood is a mixture of carbon compounds like cellulose (a carbohydrate), which decompose on heating. Most of the products formed escape, and what is left behind is mainly carbon, which is a better fuel than wood. You can prepare charcoal by heating wood shavings in a closed container that has a hole for gases to escape.

Charcoal is a better fuel than wood

(a) When the same mass of charcoal and wood are burnt, charcoal produces almost twice the heat produced by wood. So, its energy-conversion efficiency is better than that of wood.

(b) Charcoal produces much less smoke than wood.

(c) Charcoal is a compact fuel that is more convenient to handle than wood.

Cattle Dung

Cattle dung has been traditionally used as a fuel in India. The dung is shaped into flat cakes, dried and used as fuel for cooking. Burning cattle-dung cake produces some heat and a lot of smoke. Scientists have now found a better way of using cattle dung—to produce biogas, which is an excellent fuel. This gas is popularly called *gobar gas*.

Biogas

Certain types of bacteria decompose wet biomass in an oxygen-free (anaerobic) environment to produce a combustible mixture of gases, called biogas. The process is called anaerobic digestion. Biogas can contain up to 75% methane, 23% carbon dioxide and 2% other gases, including hydrogen and hydrogen sulphide. Methane is an excellent fuel.

Biogas can be produced in a biogas plant by using cattle dung, sewage, agricultural residues, and so on. It can be used for electricity generation and for cooking. A few lakh biogas plants have been built in our country.

Biogas plant

A biogas plant has a digester in which the biomass is decomposed, a mixing tank for mixing the biomass with water, an outflow tank and a means of collecting gas.

The biomass, e.g., cattle dung, is mixed with water in the mixing tank to form slurry. The slurry from this tank flows into the digester, which is a sealed chamber. The biomass decomposes here and expands, and the gas produced presses down the slurry. This causes the spent slurry to overflow into the outflow tank. The spent slurry is used as manure.

The upper part of the digester has an outlet for gas. To prevent excessive pressure build up, the gas is removed from time to time.

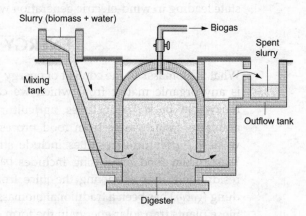

Fig. 6.6 Biogas plant

Advantages of biogas

(a) A biogas plant is quite simple and can be easily built in rural areas.

(b) Biogas is an excellent, clean fuel that burns without producing ash and smoke.

(c) The spent slurry is good manure.

(d) Biogas plants are a safe and useful way of waste disposal.

(e) Use of biogas in rural areas leads to saving of firewood, and reduces deforestation.

SOLAR ENERGY

The earth receives a huge amount of energy from the sun. Each square metre of the earth's upper atmosphere receives about 1.36 kilojoules (kJ) of solar energy per second. In other words, solar energy is incident at the rate of 1.36 kW/m^2.

The entire energy incident on the upper atmosphere of the earth does not reach its surface. About 40% of this energy is reflected by the atmosphere into space. Then some of it is absorbed by the gases and particles present in the atmosphere. Finally, only about 47% of the incident energy reaches the earth's surface.

Solar energy sustains life processes on the earth. Plants use it to make food. Traditionally we have been using solar energy for drying clothes and grains, making salt from sea water, etc. Newer uses include solar heating devices and solar cells. Solar heating devices such as solar cookers and solar water heaters use the heat energy that comes with sunlight. Solar cells convert solar energy into electricity.

Advantages of solar energy

(a) It is available everywhere.

(b) It is available in plenty (renewable), and it is free.

(c) It does not cause pollution.

Limitations of solar energy

(a) It cannot be used at night.

(b) Devices based on solar energy do not work well on cloudy days.

Solar Heating Devices

A solar heating device uses solar energy to heat things like water and food. To make a solar heating device effective, we have to ensure that the device absorbs a lot of heat from sunlight and does not lose too much of the collected heat. To achieve these, the following measures are taken.

Increasing the absorption of heat Everything on which sunlight falls absorbs heat from it. However, black and dark-coloured surfaces absorb heat better than do light-coloured and white surfaces. That is why you feel hotter than usual when you wear dark clothes in summer. You can do the following activity to see the effect of colour on the absorption of heat.

Take two cardboard boxes of the same size. Paint the inner walls of one white and paint the other black. Cover the top of the boxes with glass and keep the boxes in the sun. The glass tops will allow sunlight to enter the boxes. After 15 minutes or so, check the temperature of each box. You will find the box with black inner walls is at a higher temperature.

So, in certain types of solar heating devices, the surfaces meant for collecting sunlight are painted black to increase the absorption of heat.

Reducing the loss of heat A hot object loses heat to it surroundings by conduction, convection and radiation. Different methods are used to reduce the loss of heat in heating devices. In a box-type device, to reduce heat loss by conduction, the walls are made of an insulator, i.e., a material that is a poor conductor of heat. The box is made airtight so that the air inside cannot take the heat out of the box. Thus, convection loss is also reduced. Radiation loss is reduced by covering the top of the box with glass. Sunlight passes through the glass and heats the materials inside the box. The heated materials radiate heat, but these get reflected back into the box by the glass. This traps the heat (in the same way it is trapped in a greenhouse).

Increasing the amount of sunlight collected A reflector such as a plane mirror is used to reflect sunlight into the heating device so that more sunlight enters it.

Box-type solar cooker

A solar cooker is a device that uses solar energy for cooking. In its simplest form it consists of a special box in which the food to be cooked is placed. The box is made of an insulating material such as plastic or wood. The box may be double-walled, with an insulating material (even air) between the outer and inner walls. This reduces heat loss due to conduction more effectively. The inner walls are painted black to increase heat absorption. The box is covered with a glass sheet. This reduces heat loss by radiation and traps heat, which increases the temperature inside the box. The covered box is made airtight to reduce heat loss by convection. To increase the amount of sunlight going into the box, a plane mirror is hinged at an angle at the top of the box.

The food to be cooked is taken in a vessel and placed inside the cooker. The temperature inside the cooker reaches 100–140°C in about 2–3 hours in summer. So, you can cook food that requires slow heating like *dal*, vegetables, rice, and so on.

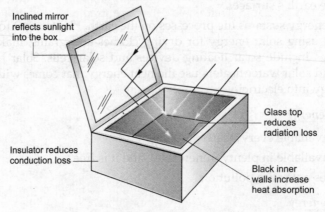

Fig. 6.7 Box-type solar cooker

Advantages Solar cookers are inexpensive to own and operate. You can put food in several vessels inside the cooker so that they get cooked simultaneously. These cookers reduce firewood and LPG consumption. And they do not produce any smoke.

Disadvantages A solar cooker can be used only during daytime. They can be used effectively only in regions with warm climate. They take a long time to cook food in winters and on cloudy days. You cannot use box-type cookers to fry food or make *roti*.

Solar water heater

Solar energy can be used to heat water. In a solar water heater, sunlight is allowed to fall on a box made of a poor conductor of heat. The glass top of the box lets in sunlight and traps heat. Water enters a tube that is painted black to increase the absorption of heat. It is bent several times to increase its length inside the box. This allows the water flowing through it sufficient time to absorb heat. Hot water collects in the tank of the heater for use.

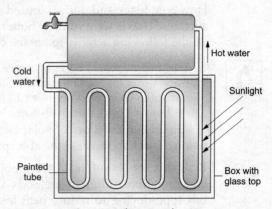

Fig. 6.8 Solar water heater

Solar Cells

A device which converts solar energy directly into electricity is called a solar cell or a photovoltaic (PV) cell. Some substances like silicon are semiconductors. Their ability to conduct electricity is much less than that of conductors. However, when certain substances are added to semiconductors, they are able to conduct electricity much better. Solar cells are made from such altered semiconductors.

When sunlight falls on a solar cell, a potential difference of about 0.5–1 V develops across it. The power of a solar cell depends on its surface area. The greater the surface area of the solar cell, the greater is the solar energy collected by it, and hence, the greater is the power generated. Small solar cells are, therefore suitable for use in only those electronic devices that require very little power. Such devices include calculators and watches. A typical solar cell delivers much less power than a common dry cell.

Solar panel

Although a solar cell provides very little power, a large number of connected solar cells, spread over a large area, can provide sufficient power for many applications. Such an arrangement of solar cells is called a solar panel. The solar cells in a solar panel are connected in such a way that the total potential difference and the total capacity to provide electric current become large.

Uses of solar panels The advantage of solar panels is more in areas where the usual energy sources are not available. That is why they are used as the source of electric power in satellites. Solar panels have also been used in unmanned aircraft that fly at high altitudes for long periods, conducting scientific experiments. Experimental solar-powered cars have also been made. In many parts of India, solar panels are being used to charge rechargeable batteries during the day. At night, these batteries provide electric power for lighting, etc. They are also being used for operating traffic lights, water pumps, telephones, TV sets and radio receivers.

Fig. 6.9 (a) An experimental solar-powered aircraft (b) Solar-powered light

Advantages of solar cells

(a) Solar cells are suitable for use in remote areas where electrical power lines have not reached.

(b) Solar cells require little maintenance and last for a long time.

(c) After installation, no further cost is involved in generating electricity directly from solar cells.

(d) Solar cells are environment friendly, as they do not cause any pollution.

Limitations of generating electricity from solar cells

(a) Solar panels are expensive. Although silicon is the second-most abundant element on earth, the cost of purifying silicon for making semiconductors used in solar cells is very high. This increases the cost of solar cells.

(b) The solar cells in a solar panel are connected using silver, to keep the resistance as low as possible. This also increases the cost.

(c) Solar cells provide direct current (DC), while most household appliances work on AC. Special devices (inverters) are needed to convert the DC to AC.

(d) Since the power output of solar cells is low, a large number of solar panels, spread over a large area, are required, even to meet the normal electrical power requirement of a household.

(e) Like all solar devices, solar cells work only during the day, and their effectiveness is reduced in winters and on cloudy days. For the power requirement at night, storage batteries are charged by solar cells during the day. The batteries further add to the cost.

ELECTRICITY FROM THE OCEAN

Electricity can be generated from the ocean by utilizing the following facts.

- Tides cause the level of sea water to rise and fall periodically. This is mainly due to the gravitational pull exerted by the moon, and to some extent by the sun. The water level is maximum at high tide and minimum at low tide. The difference in water levels can be utilized to generate electricity.

- Waves in the ocean involve a lot of kinetic energy, which can be converted to electricity.

- The water at the surface of the ocean is warmer than the water deep below. Their temperature difference can be utilized to generate electricity.

Generating Electricity from Tides

A tidal power plant can be located at the mouth of a narrow bay, where tides cause regular and appreciable rise in the level of water. A dam with gates is constructed at the mouth of the bay (Figure 6.10). At high tide, the level of the water in the bay rises, and it is allowed to flow in and collect behind the dam. When the tide ebbs, the water level in the sea starts falling. The dam gates are then closed. As a result, the level of water behind the dam remains higher than that in the bay. When the difference in the levels is sufficient, the gates of the dam are opened, and water is allowed to fall into the bay. This falling water is used to drive turbines connected to electric generators. (In some power plants, the water flowing in at high tide is also used to generate a part of the power.)

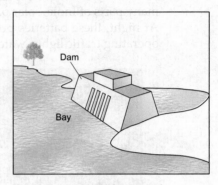

Fig. 6.10 Tidal power plant

For a tidal power plant, the difference between the water levels at high tide and low tide should be about 5 metres. Not many places have this. For this reason, tidal energy cannot be a major source of electrical power.

Generating Electricity from Ocean Waves

We can convert the energy of ocean waves into electricity at places where there are strong waves. Figure 6.11 shows schematically one setup for generating electricity from waves. A large air-filled object, called a surface follower, floats in the sea and moves up and down with the waves. It is linked to a shaft at the bottom of the sea in such a way that its up-and-down motion is converted into the rotational motion of the shaft. The rotation of the shaft is used to turn the shaft of an electric generator.

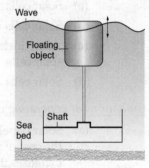

Ocean waves are caused by winds. Since winds arise due to the heating of the earth's surface by the sun, the ultimate source of energy of ocean waves is the sun.

Fig. 6.11 Surface follower

Ocean Thermal Energy Conversion (OTEC)

Solar energy falling on the surface of the ocean warms it. The water at the surface of the ocean is warmer than the water deep below. Generally, the difference in temperature is about 20°C between the surface water and the water at a depth of 1 km. This temperature difference can be used to operate an ocean thermal energy conversion (OTEC) plant. Clearly, the ultimate source of the stored thermal energy of the ocean is the sun.

In one system for OTEC, a fluid with low boiling point such as ammonia or chlorofluorocarbon (CFC) is used as the

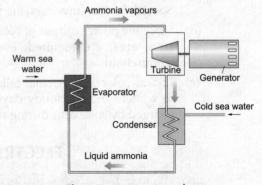

Fig. 6.12 OTEC power plant

'working fluid'. Warm sea water is used to vaporize liquid ammonia in an evaporator. The expanding vapours of ammonia turn a turbine connected to a generator. Then the vapours go to a condenser. There, cold sea water, pumped up from the deep, is used to liquefy the ammonia. This ammonia is reused, and the cycle goes on.

GEOTHERMAL ENERGY

Geothermal energy means energy stored as heat in the earth. You know that below the earth's crust lies a layer called the mantle. The temperature near the upper part of the mantle is around 1500°C. The material here is in a partially molten state and is called magma.

In some areas, hot magma swells up into the crust, but remains trapped below the surface of the earth. Such areas in the earth's crust are called hot spots. The rocks and groundwater above these hot spots get heated. At some places, the hot water comes to the surface and collects in pools called hot springs. In some cases, the water gets converted to

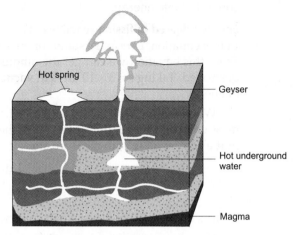

Fig. 6.13 Geysers and hot springs

steam. Steam or steam mixed with hot water pushes out of the surface of the earth with great force. The fountain of steam and water coming out from the surface of the earth is called a geyser. Steam as well as hot water from geothermal sources can be utilized by us. Some common uses include heating of buildings and generation of electricity.

Generating Electricity from Geothermal Energy

At places where dry steam comes out of the surface of the earth, it can be used directly to turn turbines connected to generators. The world's largest geothermal electric power plant, at Geysers Steam Field, California, uses this method to generate electricity. At places where steam does not come out on its own, arrangements are made to convert the hot underground water into steam. The steam is then used to turn turbines.

Advantages of geothermal energy

(a) Geothermal plants can operate round the clock, unlike those based on solar and tidal energy.

(b) Geothermal energy is almost pollution free.

(c) It is cheaper to run a geothermal plant than a coal-based plant.

(d) The source of energy is free and renewable.

NUCLEAR ENERGY

Nuclear Fission

In about 400 power plants worldwide, electricity is produced from the energy liberated in a special type of nuclear reaction called nuclear fission. The word 'fission' means to split or break up into parts. Nuclear fission is a reaction in which a heavy nucleus splits into two middleweight nuclei, releasing a lot of energy.

The process of a heavy nucleus splitting into two middleweight nuclei is called nuclear fission.

One of the isotopes of uranium is U-235 (235 is its mass number, i.e., the sum of the number of neutrons and protons). The nucleus of U-235 can be used to start a nuclear fission reaction by bombarding it with slow-moving neutrons. In this process, *U-235 itself does not undergo fission*. It converts to U-236, which is highly unstable. As soon as it forms, U-236 splits in two parts, i.e., it fissions. Some neutrons, generally 2 or 3, are also emitted in this process.

The nuclei of the elements formed by fission are unstable. They disintegrate further to form stable nuclei. Gamma ray (electromagnetic radiation) and particles such as neutrons and electrons are emitted by the nuclei at different stages between the fission and the creation of stable nuclei.

In the fission of uranium, the combined mass of the fission products is less than the combined mass of the neutron and the U-235 nucleus, with which the reaction started. This loss in mass gets converted into energy.

Energy released in fission reactions You must have heard of Einstein's famous equation, $E = mc^2$. In this equation, E, m and c stand for energy, mass and the speed of light in vacuum respectively. From this equation we can get the amount of energy released when matter of a certain mass is destroyed. Taking $c = 3 \times 10^8$ m/s in vacuum, 1 kg of disappearing mass will give rise to 9×10^{16} J of energy.

When dealing with atoms and nuclei, scientists prefer to measure mass in a unit called atomic mass unit (u), which is defined as $\frac{1}{12}$ of the mass of one atom of carbon-12. And they often use the unit electronvolt (eV) to measure energy.

$$1 \text{ u} \approx 1.67 \times 10^{-27} \text{ kg.}$$

$$1 \text{ eV} \approx 1.6 \times 10^{-19} \text{ J.}$$

It turns out that 1 u of mass, when converted into energy, releases about 931 MeV of energy.

How much energy do we get from the fission of one uranium nucleus? From the fission of one U-236 nucleus, we get about 200×10^6 eV (200 MeV) of energy. To get an idea of the amount of energy liberated by fission, let us do a comparison with energy released by burning coal. When 1 g of coal is burnt completely, 30 kJ of energy is produced. A fission reaction that consumes 1 g of U-235 produces 8.3×10^7 kJ of energy!

The energy released in nuclear fission can be used to generate electricity as well as to make atom bombs.

Chain Reactions

Suppose a slow neutron is absorbed by a nucleus of U-235 in a block of uranium. The resulting U-236 nucleus fissions, and in the process 2 or 3 neutrons are emitted. These neutrons can be absorbed by other U-235 nuclei, starting other fission reactions, from which neutrons are emitted. In this way, the fission reaction continues by itself, without requiring any further external neutrons. One fission triggers another fission, in a self-sustaining sequence of fission reactions.

A reaction that continues on its own as one occurrence of the reaction triggers the next occurrence is called a chain reaction.

A chain reaction in 1 kg of U-235 will cause the fission of all its nuclei in less than one minute. This will release a tremendous amount of energy in a very short time, leading to an explosion. Fortunately, the rate of a chain reaction can be controlled with materials that absorb neutrons. This is done when fission is used in nuclear power plants.

Generating Electricity at Nuclear Power Plants

To generate electricity, nuclear fission is carried out in a setup called a nuclear reactor. The energy released is used to generate steam, which drives turbines connected to generators. The whole system, including the nuclear reactor, the turbine, etc., is called a nuclear power plant.

Advantages and Disadvantages of Nuclear Power

Advantages

(a) Nuclear power plants consume very little fuel.

(b) If operated properly, nuclear power plants produce less atmospheric pollution than thermal power plants.

(c) A sizeable amount of fuel can be reclaimed by processing the spent fuel material. In contrast, fuels like coal cannot be reclaimed once they have been used.

(d) Some radioactive isotopes are produced as by-products in the process, and these are used in medicine and industry.

(e) Nuclear power is a viable option where fossil fuels like coal are not available, or where it is not possible to generate electricity from wind, water, etc.

Disadvantages

(a) A lot of radioactive and toxic wastes are produced in the different stages of energy production from nuclear fission. They cannot be simply thrown away. So, they are stored in long-term underground storage facilities, which are expensive to build.

(b) In case of accidents, nuclear radiation may affect those near the site. Radioactive materials that may leak out can contaminate vast areas of land, crops, water bodies, etc.

(c) Nuclear power plants cannot be located near populated areas.

(d) Nuclear power plants are expensive to build.

(e) Nuclear power plants also pose security problems, as the fuel and by-products can be used to build nuclear weapons.

Nuclear Fusion

You have seen that when a heavy nucleus breaks into two middleweight nuclei, a lot of energy is liberated. Energy is also liberated when two light nuclei combine to form a single nucleus. This process is called nuclear fusion.

The process of two or more light nuclei combining to form a heavier nucleus is called nuclear fusion.

An example of nuclear fusion is given below.

$$\underset{\text{(dueteron)}}{^{2}_{1}\text{H}} \; + \; \underset{}{^{2}_{1}\text{H}} \; \rightarrow \; \underset{\text{(helium - 3)}}{^{3}_{2}\text{He}} \; + \; \underset{\text{(neutron)}}{\text{n}} \; + \; \text{energy}$$

Deuteron is the nucleus of deuterium, an isotope of hydrogen. Two deuterons combine to form the nucleus of helium-3, an isotope of helium. In this reaction, the mass of the product nucleus is less than the combined mass of the starting nuclei. The difference of mass is converted to energy, given by $E = mc^2$.

The energy of the sun comes from nuclear fusion in which, in a series of reactions, hydrogen gets converted into helium. This is accompanied by the release of a huge amount of energy.

We have plenty of hydrogen on the earth. Is it possible to use it to get energy from fusion? Scientists are working hard to produce usable energy from fusion reactions. However, the high temperature (about 10^7 K) required for fusion causes problems. All materials vapourize at that temperature. So, you cannot even have a solid container to hold the particles for fusion!

Fusion has been used to make nuclear bombs that are more powerful than those based on fission. These are called hydrogen bombs or thermonuclear bombs. To start fusion, a small fission bomb is used as the first-stage of the thermonuclear bomb. Its blast creates the high temperature and pressure required for fusion.

USING ENERGY JUDICIOUSLY

The total coal reserves in our country are estimated to be about 80 billion tonnes, but we are consuming it at a rate of 250 million tonnes per year. At this rate the resource that nature produced over millions of years will be consumed in just a few hundred years! The situation is more alarming in the case of oil (petroleum) reserves. The known oil reserves of our country are about 500 million tonnes only, of which we are consuming 30 million tonnes per year. So, the oil reserves will last for a few decades only.

The demand for energy is increasing every day. The increasing demand cannot be met for a long time unless new resources are harnessed, since conventional, nonrenewable energy sources are depleting very fast. This situation is called energy crisis. Increased use of fossil fuels is also causing environmental problems such as air pollution which leads to health problems, acid rain and global warming.

To overcome the energy crisis and to save the environment, we have to use energy judiciously. This means *using less of nonrenewable and more of renewable energy sources, not wasting energy and saving energy wherever possible.*

We can stop the wastage of energy, for example, by switching off lights, fans, coolers, etc., when they are not in use. In large cities, sharing a car with other people going to work in the same area or using public transport can save a lot of fuel. Many such commonsense things can be done to save energy. Think about this: making sure that taps do not leak saves the energy used in pumping extra water.

· POINTS TO REMEMBER ·

- *Good Sources of Energy*
  Characteristics:
  (a) high energy output per unit volume (or mass),
  (b) steady availability,
  (c) safe and easy to use,
  (d) easy to store and transport,
  (e) economical

- *Classification of sources of energy*
  Renewable sources of energy are those which can be generated by us or which are constantly being generated by natural processes or whose supply is unlimited. Examples: the sun, wind, flowing water.

  Nonrenewable sources of energy are those which were produced in the past by natural processes, whose supply is limited and which we cannot generate ourselves. Examples: coal, petroleum, natural gas.

  Sources of energy that have been in use for centuries are called *conventional sources of energy*. Examples: wood, coal, petroleum and flowing water.

  Sources of energy that we have started using in new ways or only in recent times are called *nonconventional* or *alternate sources of energy*. Examples: solar, geothermal, tidal, wave and nuclear energy.

- *Fossil fuels*
  Fuels that originated from the remains of dead plants and animals are called fossil fuels. Coal, petroleum and natural gas are fossil fuels. These are conventional, nonrenewable fuels. Burning them causes air pollution. The pollutants produced include carbon dioxide, carbon monoxide, oxides of nitrogen, sulphur dioxide and unburnt particles. The oxides of nitrogen and sulphur cause acid rain. Natural gas is the cleanest fossil fuel.

- *Energy from flowing water*
  Flowing water has kinetic energy, which can be used to do useful work. This principle is used to generate hydroelectricity. Water is collected behind dams and is allowed to fall down on the blades of turbines connected to generators.

  Advantages: Free and renewable source of energy . nonpolluting . cost of electricity generation is lower than that from thermal and nuclear plants . flowing water is more reliable than wind . hydroelectricity can be generated on a large scale from a single plant . dams built for hydroelectric plants also help in flood control and irrigation . small hydroelectric plants are best options for generating electricity from renewable sources, as they do not affect the environment much

  Disadvantages: Large dams affect the plants and animals of the region . large hydroelectric power plants are expensive to build . not all rivers and areas are suitable for hydroelectric power generation

- *Wind energy*
  Wind is caused by the uneven heating of the earth's surface by the sun. To generate electricity on a commercial basis, wind-electric generators are set up in large wind farms.

  Advantages: Free source of energy . nonpolluting . factories can use small wind-electric plants

  Limitations: Requires regular wind . is not a dependable source . wind farms are costly

- *Energy from biomass*
  In the context of energy production, biomass means any organic matter from which we can get energy on a renewable basis. Wood is a biomass fuel. Wood can be more efficiently utilized by converting it into charcoal.

  Biogas is a combustible mixture of gases produced by the decomposition of biomass. It is produced by the anaerobic digestion of biomass such as cattle dung, sewage, etc. Biogas can contain up to 75% methane, 23% carbon dioxide and 2% other gases, including hydrogen and hydrogen sulphide. This combustible mixture is an excellent renewable fuel that can be used for electricity generation and for cooking.

  Advantages of biogas: biogas plants are simple . biogas is an excellent, clean fuel that burns without producing ash and smoke . the spent slurry is good manure . biogas plants are a safe and useful way of waste disposal . use of biogas leads to saving of firewood, and reduces deforestation.

- *Solar energy*
  The energy received from the sun is called solar energy. The sun is the ultimate source of energy of fossil fuels, flowing water, wind, biomass and ocean waves.

Advantages: Is available everywhere • is available in plenty and is free • nonpolluting

Limitations: It cannot be used at night • devices based on solar energy do not work well on cloudy days.

A solar heating device uses solar energy to heat things like water and food. A solar heating device can be made effective by (a) increasing the absorption of heat, (b) reducing the loss of heat, and (c) increasing and concentrating the sunlight collected.

• *Solar cookers*

A box-type solar cooker is an insulated, air-tight box covered with glass. Its inner surface is painted black, and it has a plain mirror to increase incident sunlight.

Advantages: Inexpensive to own and operate, can cook food in several vessels simultaneously, reduces firewood and LPG consumption, does not produce smoke

Disadvantages: Can be used only during daytime, effective only in warm climates, ineffective in winters and on cloudy days, cannot use box-type cookers to fry food or make *roti.*

• *Solar cells*

A device which converts solar energy directly into electricity is called a *solar cell.* Solar cells are made from semiconductors like silicon. In a *solar panel,* a large number of solar cells are connected to get a large potential difference and current. Uses: in calculators, watches, artificial satellites, and in providing electricity in remote areas to run such things as pumps, telephones, lights, etc.

Advantages: Suitable for remote areas with no electricity, requires little maintenance, low operating cost, pollution-free operation

Limitations: Expensive, provides only DC, requires large area for generating even modest amount of power, works only in daytime, reduced efficiency in winters and on cloudy days

• *Electricity from the ocean*

In *tidal power plants,* water of the rising tide is collected in a reservoir. When the tide ebbs, the difference in levels of water in the reservoir and the sea is used to make water fall on turbines.

Surface followers are devices that move up and down with the waves, and this motion is converted to rotary motion, used for turning the shaft of a generator.

In an ocean, the difference in temperature between the surface water and the water at a depth of 1 km is about 20°C. This temperature difference is used to operate an ocean thermal energy conversion (OTEC) plant. Liquid ammonia (or CFC) heated by warm sea water evaporates and expands to turn a turbine. The vapours are condensed back to liquid by cold sea water, and reused.

• *Geothermal energy*

Geothermal energy is the energy stored as heat in the earth. It heats rocks and water below the ground. Above hot spots, dry steam or a mixture of steam and hot water come out. The steam can be used directly to turn turbines. At other places, different methods are used to get steam from the underground hot water.

• *Nuclear energy*

The process of a heavy nucleus splitting into two middleweight nuclei is called *nuclear fission.* U-235 absorbs a slow neutron to become U-236, which splits (fissions) to give about 200 MeV of energy.

A reaction that continues on its own as one occurrence of the reaction triggers the next occurrence is called a *chain reaction.* Controlled chain reaction is used in nuclear power plants.

To generate electricity, the energy released by nuclear fission in a nuclear reactor is used to generate steam, which drives turbines connected to generators.

The process of two or more light nuclei combining to form a heavier nucleus is called *nuclear fusion.* Energy in the sun is produced by the fusion of hydrogen into helium. Scientists are working hard to produce energy from fusion reactions. The high temperatures (about 10^7 K) required for fusion is posing many problems.

· EXERCISES ·

A. *Very-Short-Answer Questions*

1. Name two renewable and two nonrenewable sources of energy.

2. Name two conventional and two nonconventional sources of energy.

3. What is the ultimate source of the energy of fossil fuels?

4. Name four fuels that we get from fossil fuels.

5. Among fossil fuels, which is the least polluting?

6. What happens when coal burns incompletely?

7. What is a turbine?

8. What is hydroelectricity?

9. Mention two ways by which water can be used to produce hydroelectricity. (2001)

10. What kind of energy does wind possess?

11. In the context of energy production, what is biomass?

12. What is the main constituent of biogas?

13. Which will cause the least amount of smoke when burnt—wood, cattle-dung cakes or biogas?

14. Why is solar energy considered renewable?

15. If 100 joules of solar energy is received by the upper atmosphere, how much of it reaches the earth's surface?

16. What is a solar heating device?

17. In a box-type solar cooker what is the range of temperature that can be achieved in two to three hours?   **(1995, '97)**

18. Why is the inside surface of a box-type solar cooker blackened?

19. A solar cell transforms energy of one form into another form. What are these two forms of energy?   **(1995)**

20. What is a solar panel?

21. Can a solar panel be used directly to power the TV set in your home?

22. What is geothermal energy?   **(1992)**

23. What is nuclear fission?

24. What is a chain reaction?

25. What is nuclear fusion?

26. What is a nuclear reactor?   **(2006)**

27. Name the process by which the sun produces its energy.   **(2006)**

28. Which process is carried out at a higher temperature: nuclear fusion or nuclear fission?   **(1992, '94)**

29. Give an example of how you can stop the wastage of energy.

B. *Short-Answer Questions*

1. Why are fossil fuels considered nonrenewable?

2. Can the excessive use of coal have a deteriorating effect on structures like the Taj Mahal? If yes, in what way?

3. How is charcoal produced?

4. Why is charcoal a better fuel than wood?

5. (a) Name the four gases commonly present in biogas. (b) List two advantages of using biogas over fossil fuels.   **(2006)**

6. When we harness wind energy, we harness solar energy indirectly. Explain.   **(2002)**

7. How is electricity produced from wind energy? What are wind farms?

8. What are the advantages and limitations of wind energy?

9. Give two reasons why hydroelectricity is preferable to electricity from a coal-based plant.   **(2003)**

10. Where are tidal power plants usually located? What are the limitations of tidal power?

11. Draw a diagram to show the basic design of a box-type solar cooker.   **(2000)**

12. Explain the role of the glass top in a box type solar cooker.

13. What are the limitations of solar heating devices?

14. What are the advantages of solar energy?

15. Describe three uses of a solar panel.

16. What is the difficulty in the large-scale use of solar cells in electricity production?

17. How can electricity be generated from waves?

18. How are the wastes produced in nuclear power plants different from those produced at other power plants? What happens to the waste?

C. *Long-Answer Questions*

1. What is the difference between renewable and nonrenewable sources of energy?

2. What are the characteristics of a good energy source?

3. What are the problems caused by burning fossil fuels?

4. Describe the construction and working of a biogas plant.

5. Why is hydro energy considered an indirect source of solar energy? Explain how hydro energy can be converted into electrical energy. State two advantages of hydro energy.   **(1996)**

6. What causes wind to blow? Name a part of India where wind energy is commercially harnessed. Compare wind power and the power of flowing water for generating electricity. What are the hindrances in developing them?   **(2006)**

7. Discuss the advantages and disadvantages of generating electricity from the wind.

8. Describe a box-type solar cooker, mentioning how the loss of heat is reduced in it.

9. Briefly discuss three principles based on which electricity can be generated from the ocean.

10. Describe how the difference in temperatures at different depths of the ocean can be utilized for generating electricity.

11. What are the problems created by the increased demand of energy? How can we solve them?

D. *Objective Questions*

I. *Pick the correct option.*

1. Which of the following is a renewable source of energy?
   (a) Coal   (b) Natural gas
   (c) Wood   (d) Petroleum

2. The purpose of the glass cover on top of a box-type solar cooker is to
   (a) allow one to see the food being cooked
   (b) allow more sunlight into the box

(c) prevent dust from entering the box

(d) reduce heat loss by radiation

3. A solar panel is made by combining a large number of
    (a) solar cookers   (b) solar cells
    (c) solar water heaters   (d) solar concentrators

4. To work properly, wind-electric generators need wind speeds of at least about
    (a) 1.5 km/h   (b) 15 km/h
    (c) 150 km/h   (d) 1500 km/h

5. The site of a hydroelectric plant should be chosen carefully because it
    (a) produces a large amount of carbon monoxide and carbon dioxide
    (b) produces a large amount of electricity
    (c) affects the organisms of the region
    (d) is expensive

6. Electricity from the ocean can be generated based on utilizing
    (a) kinetic energy of the waves but not stored thermal energy
    (b) stored thermal energy but not kinetic energy of the waves
    (c) kinetic energy of the waves as well as stored thermal energy
    (d) neither kinetic energy of the waves nor stored thermal energy

7. Which energy is not derived from the sun?
    (a) Nuclear energy   (b) Wind energy
    (c) Biomass energy   (d) Ocean-wave energy

8. Which of the following is not biomass?
    (a) Sun   (b) Rice husk
    (c) Wood   (d) Cattle dung

9. The condition for producing biogas is
    (a) air but not water   (b) water but not air
    (c) air and water   (d) neither air nor water

10. Geothermal energy is feasible in regions that
    (a) are near the sea   (b) have thermal plants
    (c) have coal mines
    (d) are over hot spots in the crust

II. *Fill in the blanks.*

1. A device transforming solar energy directly into electricity is called a ....

2. Wind is caused due to the ...... heating of air near the earth's surface.

3. Hydro energy is ...... reliable than wind energy.

4. The heat stored below the earth's surface is called ...... energy.

5. The main constituent of charcoal is ....

6. One important by-product of a biogas plant is ....

7. Solar cells are made from special materials called ....

8. A nuclear reaction in uranium starts when a slow-moving ...... is absorbed by the nucleus of U-235.

· ANSWERS ·

D. *Objective Questions*

I.   **1.** (c)   **2.** (d)   **3.** (b)   **4.** (b)   **5.** (c)

     6. (c)   **7.** (a)   **8.** (a)   **9.** (b)   **10.** (d)

❖

Question Bank

Includes questions that require higher-order thinking skills (HOTS)

LIGHT (REFLECTION, REFRACTION, DISPERSION AND SCATTERING)

Objective Questions

I. *Pick the correct option.*

1. The speed of light is shown in the figure by the point A. The point O represents zero speed. The point on the line representing speed of sound should be drawn

    (a) just to the right of O

    (b) at the middle of O and A

    (c) just to the left of A

    (d) to the right of A

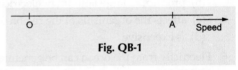

Fig. QB-1

2. Light falls obliquely on the surface of a thick glass slab as shown in the figure. Which statement among the following is correct?

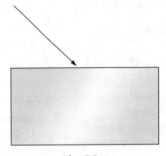

Fig. QB-2

    (a) Light stops at the surface.

    (b) Light reflects at the surface but does not refract.

    (c) Light refracts at the surface but does not reflect.

    (d) A part of the light reflects at the surface and a part of it refracts.

3. A real image of a point object is formed in a mirror when

    (a) the incident rays actually intersect

    (b) the reflected rays actually intersect

    (c) the incident rays seem to diverge from a point

    (d) the reflected rays seem to diverge from a point

4. A lens is fitted inside a tube. A parallel beam of light enters the tube, goes through the lens and emerges as a divergent beam, as shown in Figure QB-3. The lens in the tube

Fig. QB-3

    (a) must be concave   (b) must be convex

    (c) may be convex or concave (d) cannot produce the emergent beam

126

5. The four figures below show a concave mirror whose focus is *F* and the centre of curvature is *C*. *CD* is an object. Which figure correctly represents its image *CE*?

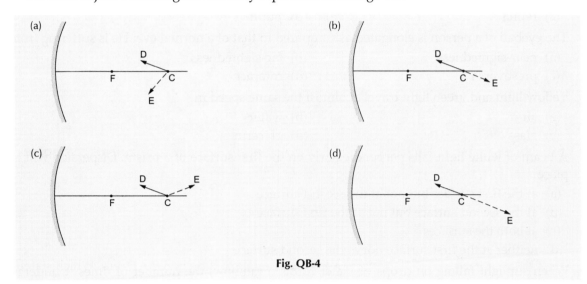

Fig. QB-4

6. Light passes from a medium *A* to another medium *B* without bending at the interface. Which of the following is not possible?
    (a) *A* and *B* have the same refractive index and light falls on the interface obliquely.
    (b) *A* and *B* have the same refractive index and light falls on the interface perpendicularly.
    (c) *A* and *B* have different refractive indices and light falls normally on the interface.
    (d) *A* and *B* have different refractive indices and light falls obliquely on the interface.

7. When a convex lens forms an image whose size is equal to that of the object, the object is placed
    (a) at a distance less than *f*   (b) between *f* and 2*f*
    (c) at 2*f*   (d) beyond 2*f*

8. A convex lens forms an image some distance away from the lens. If the image is erect, the object is placed
    (a) at a distance less than *f*   (b) between *f* and 2*f*
    (c) at 2*f*   (d) beyond 2*f*

9. The power of a convex lens of focal length 5 cm is
    (a) +20 D   (b) +50 D
    (c) –20 D   (d) –50 D

10. The ability of the eye to adjust the focal length of the eye-lens to form sharp images is called
    (a) distinct vision   (b) dilation
    (c) accommodation   (d) hyperopia

11. The eye adjusts the focal length of the eye-lens with the help of
    (a) accommodation   (b) ciliary muscles
    (c) retina   (d) cornea

12. The standard value of the least distance of distinct vision is
    (a) 20 mm   (b) 20 cm
    (c) 25 mm   (d) 25 cm

13. A lady is prescribed bifocal lenses. She is suffering from
    (a) near-sightedness only
    (b) far-sightedness only
    (c) both hypermetropia and hyperopia
    (d) both near-sightedness and far-sightedness

14. When light enters the eye and is focused on the retina, most of the bending occurs at the
    (a) cornea   (b) crystalline lens
    (c) retina   (d) pupil

15. The eyeball of a person is elongated as compared to that of a normal eye. He is suffering from
    (a) near-sightedness   (b) far-sightedness
    (c) presbyopia   (d) cataract

16. Yellow light and green light travel at almost the same speed in
    (a) air   (b) water
    (c) glass   (d) glycerin

17. A beam of white light falls perpendicularly on the first surface of a prism. Dispersion will take place
    (a) at the first surface but not at the second surface
    (b) at the second surface but not at the first surface
    (c) at both the surfaces
    (d) neither at the first surface nor at the second surface

18. When sunlight falling on drops of water forms a rainbow, the number of times it undergoes refraction at a drop is
    (a) one   (b) two
    (c) three   (d) four

19. A little milk mixed in water makes the path of a laser beam passing through it visible. This is because
    (a) milk has more density than water
    (b) milk has a larger refractive index than water
    (c) milk has fat particles which scatter light
    (d) milk is soluble in water

20. The sun appears red at sunrise and white when it is overhead at noon because
    (a) the distance between the sun and the earth is greater at sunrise than at noon
    (b) the distance between the sun and the earth is lesser at sunrise than at noon
    (c) sunlight has to travel a lesser distance in the atmosphere at sunrise than at noon
    (d) sunlight has to travel a greater distance in the atmosphere at sunrise than at noon

II. *Mark the statements True (T) or False (F).*

1. Total internal reflection is involved in the formation of a rainbow.

2. In the formation of a rainbow, when sunlight is incident on a raindrop, a part of the incident sunlight gets reflected.

3. The dimensions of the crystalline lens of the eye may change to form a sharp image but the size of the pupil never changes.

4. Light enters the eye and is refracted only when it falls on the crystalline lens.

5. The amount of light going into the eye is controlled by the iris–pupil combination.

6. If the near point of the eye is at a distance farther than the normal, the person suffers from near-sightedness.

7. A lens that cannot form an image on a screen is a concave lens.

8. A mirror that cannot form an image on a screen is a concave mirror.

9. A convex mirror gives a wider view than a plane mirror of the same size.

10. Dentists use a convex mirror to examine teeth because it forms a magnified image.

III. *Below each item in the first column write the numbers of the appropriate items from the other two columns to match. One has been done for you. (f = focal length, r = radius of curvature)*

Object position and mirror/lens type	Image position	Image type
A. 5 cm in front of a plane mirror ii, 2, 3, 7	i. At infinity	1. Real
B. 10 cm from a concave mirror of $f = 5$ cm	ii. 5 cm from the mirror	2. Virtual
	iii. 30 cm from the lens	3. Erect
C. Object at infinity for a convex mirror of $f = 15$ cm	iv. 10 cm from the mirror	4. Inverted
	v. 5 cm from the lens	5. Smaller than object
D. 30 cm from a convex lens of $f = 15$ cm	vi. 15 cm from the lens	6. Larger than object
	vii. 15 cm from the mirror	7. Same size
		8. Point-sized

Very-Short-Answer Questions

1. Which of the two mirrors shown below has a larger radius of curvature?

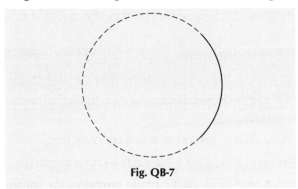

(a)   (b)

Fig. QB-5

2. The diagram below shows a ray of light getting reflected by a concave mirror. Mark the position of the focus (*F*) and the centre of curvature (*C*) on the diagram.

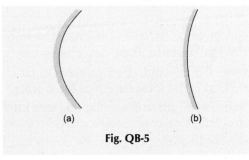

Fig. QB-6

3. The diagram below shows a concave mirror by a thick line. The sphere from which the mirror was cut is shown by a dotted line. (a) Mark the position of the focus (*F*) and the centre of curvature (*C*) on the diagram. (b) Using a ruler find the focal length of the mirror.

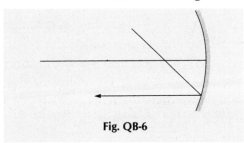

Fig. QB-7

4. A beam of light is incident on two different media, as shown in Figure QB-8. The angle of incidence is the same in the two cases. In which of the two media is the speed of light more?

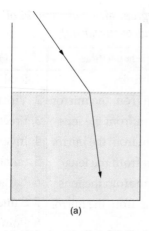
(a)

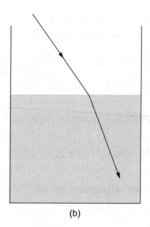
(b)

Fig. QB-8

5. Draw a diagram showing partial internal reflection as light goes from one medium to another.

6. A lens forms a 20-cm-high image of a 12-cm-high object. What kind of lens is it, convex or concave?

7. An object is placed at a distance of 20 cm from a mirror. The mirror forms an image which is of the same size as the object. What kind of mirror can it be—plane, convex or concave?

8. An object is placed at a distance of 30 cm from a concave mirror. The mirror forms an image of the same size as the object. What is the focal length of the mirror?

9. An object is placed at a distance of 20 cm from a lens. The lens forms an image of the same size as the object. What kind of lens can it be—convex or concave?

10. The magnification for a spherical mirror is given by $m = -v/u$. Explain why magnification is positive for a convex mirror.

11. The figure shows the different shapes of the crystalline lens of the eye when looking by turn at two objects at different distances. In which case is the object at a larger distance from the eye?

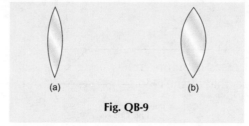
(a)   (b)

Fig. QB-9

12. The near point of a man is at 20 cm and the far point is at infinity. Does he need spectacles? If yes, should he be prescribed convex lenses or concave lenses?

13. The ciliary muscles of a person have become weak. What kind of lens does he need to read a newspaper?

Short-Answer Questions

1. Why is one surface of a mirror silvered? What will happen to the image if the silvering gets scratched at several places?

2. Can you capture an image formed by a convex mirror on (a) a screen, (b) on a camera?

3. Name two defects of vision that can be corrected with the help of lenses. Name the kind of lens used to correct each of these defects.

Long-Answer Questions

1. Look at Figure QB-10. It shows a concave mirror. F is the focus of the mirror, C is its centre of curvature and A is a point object. Draw two rays from A that fall on the mirror and show the paths of these rays after reflection. From this, locate the image of A. Do this as accurately as you can.

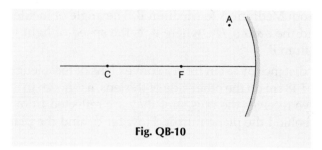

Fig. QB-10

2. Why does a properly cut diamond shine more than a similarly cut piece of glass?

3. Write the coordinate sign convention for image formation by a thin spherical lens.

4. An object *AB* of size 2 cm is placed at a distance of 20 cm from a concave lens of focal length 20 cm. The object is placed perpendicular to the principal axis, with the end *A* on the principal axis. Taking 1 cm of drawing to represent 2 cm of actual length, draw a neat diagram showing the paths of two rays from *B*, one parallel to the principal axis and the other going through the optical centre of the lens.

5. Show that the angle of deviation of a ray transmitted through a prism is equal to the sum of angles through which it bends at the first surface and the second surface.

6. Figure QB-11 shows a ray of light going through a prism. Measure the angle of deviation.

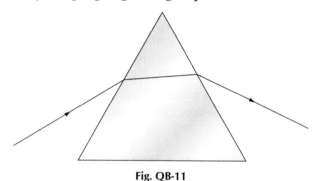

Fig. QB-11

7. Figure QB-12 shows two cases of white light falling on a glass prism. In which case will the dispersion of light be more, that is, the colours get separated better? Explain why.

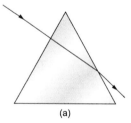

(a)

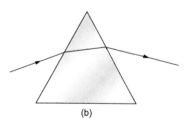

(b)

Fig. QB-12

8. What do you understand by scattering of light?

9. Some smoke looks bluish while some looks whitish. What makes them look different?

Numerical Problems

1. A spherical mirror forms a real image of an object that is 3 times as big as the object.
   (a) Is the mirror convex or concave?
   (b) Is the image erect or inverted?
   (c) If the focal length of the mirror is 15 cm, at what distance is the object placed from the figure?

2. A ray of light goes from Medium A to Medium B. The angle of incidence is 30° and the angle of refraction is 45°. Find the ratio v_A/v_B, where v_A is the speed of light in Medium A and v_B is the speed of light in Medium B.

3. An object is kept at a distance of 36 cm from a convex lens of focal length 12 cm. A plane mirror is placed at a distance of 48 cm on the other side of the lens, as shown in the figure. The ray diagram is also shown. The eye receives the rays after they are reflected from the plane mirror. The eye sees the final image behind the plane mirror. How far behind the plane mirror does this image form?

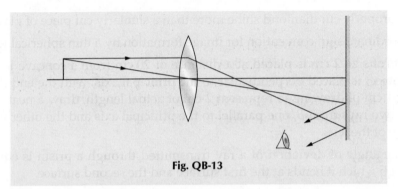

Fig. QB-13

4. An object is placed 60 cm from a screen. Where should you place a convex lens of focal length 15 cm to get the image of the object on the screen?

5. An object of size 2 cm is placed 54 cm from a screen. A convex lens of focal length 12 cm is placed between the two such that the image of the object forms on the screen. Find the two possible positions of the lens, and for each position find the size of the image.

6. A concave lens of focal length 20 cm is placed at a distance of 20 cm from a 2-cm object which is placed perpendicular to the principal axis. Find the size of the image formed.

· ANSWERS ·

Objective Questions

I. 1. (a)   2. (d)   3. (b)   4. (c)   5. (d)   6. (d)
    7. (c)   8. (a)   9. (a)   10. (c)   11. (b)   12. (d)
    13. (d)   14. (a)   15. (a)   16. (a)   17. (b)   18. (b)
    19. (c)   20. (d)

II. 1. F   2. T   3. F   4. F   5. T   6. F
    7. T   8. F   9. T   10. F

III. B. iv, 1, 4, 7   C. vii, 2, 8   D. iii, 1, 4, 7

Numerical Problems

1. (a) concave (b) inverted (c) 20 cm

2. $\dfrac{1}{\sqrt{2}}$

3. 30 cm

4. at the mid-point between the object and the lens

5. (a) 18 cm from the object, 4 cm (b) 36 cm from the object, 1 cm

6. 10 cm

ELECTRICITY, MAGNETIC EFFECT OF ELECTRIC CURRENT AND SOURCES OF ENERGY

Objective Questions

I. *Pick the correct option.*

1. 1 coulomb × 1 … = 1 joule. The missing word is
   - (a) volt
   - (b) ampere
   - (c) ohm
   - (d) watt

2. The direction of current in a wire is
   - (a) the same as the direction of the flow of electrons through the wire
   - (b) opposite to the direction of flow of the electrons through the wire
   - (c) the same as the direction of flow of the neutrons through the wire
   - (d) opposite to the direction of flow of neutrons through the wire

3. Ampere is the same as
   - (a) volt/second
   - (b) watt/second
   - (c) joule/second
   - (d) coulomb/second

4. To get a constant nonzero potential difference between the two contacts of a bulb, you should join the contacts to
   - (a) a copper wire
   - (b) a plastic wire
   - (c) an electrical socket in your house
   - (d) the terminals of a battery

5. Carbon is a
   - (a) conductor in its graphite form but insulator in its diamond form
   - (b) insulator in its graphite form but conductor in its diamond form
   - (c) conductor in both its graphite and diamond forms
   - (d) insulator in both its graphite and diamond forms

6. Pick the correct statement.
   - (a) An electric field has a direction and so does a magnetic field.
   - (b) An electric field has a direction, but a magnetic field does not.
   - (c) A magnetic field has a direction, but an electric field does not.
   - (d) Neither an electric field nor a magnetic field has a direction.

7. For the figure given below, which statement is correct?

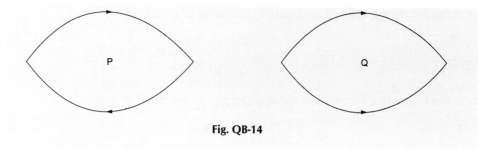

Fig. QB-14

   - (a) Both P and Q can represent a magnetic field line.
   - (b) P can represent a magnetic field line, but Q cannot.
   - (c) Q can represent a magnetic field line, but P cannot.
   - (d) Neither can represent a magnetic field line.

8. Consider a bar magnet placed in a lab. The magnetic field due to this magnet
   (a) will exist outside the magnet, but not inside it
   (b) will exist inside the magnet, but not outside it
   (c) will exist both outside and inside the magnet
   (d) will exist only near the ends

9. (•) is the symbol for
   (a) a resistor   (b) a fuse
   (c) a bulb   (d) a plug key (ON)

10. Look at the figure below and pick the correct statement.

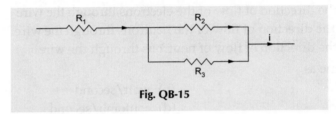

Fig. QB-15

   (a) R_1 and R_2 are connected in series.
   (b) R_1 and R_2 are connected in parallel.
   (c) R_2 and R_3 are connected in series.
   (d) R_2 and R_3 are connected in parallel.

11. Look at the figure below and pick the correct statement.

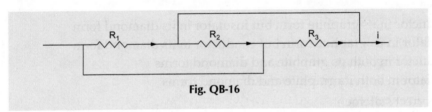

Fig. QB-16

   (a) R_1, R_2 and R_3 are joined in series.
   (b) R_1, R_2 and R_3 are joined in parallel.
   (c) R_1 and R_2 are joined in series, and R_3 is joined in parallel to their combination.
   (d) R_1 and R_2 are joined in parallel, and R_3 is joined in series with their combination.

12. Which of the following masses is closest to the mass of a proton?
   (a) 10^{-27} kg   (b) 10^{-31} kg
   (c) 10^{-19} kg   (d) 10^{-15} kg

13. Which of the following elements is most widely used for nuclear fission?
   (a) $_1^1\text{H}$ (b) $_1^3\text{H}$
   (c) ^{56}Fe (d) ^{235}U

14. As a metal filament gets heated, its resistance increases. When a potential difference of 100 volts is applied across a filament bulb, the current flowing through it is found to be 0.4 A. When a

potential difference of 200 volts is applied across the same bulb, it glows more. The current in the bulb can be expected to be

   (a) 1.6 A   (b) 0.8 A

   (c) less than 0.8 A   (d) more than 0.8 A

15. A 2-A current flows through a resistor when a potential difference of 20 V is applied across it. The resistance of the resistor is

   (a) $2\,\Omega$ (b) $1\,\Omega$

   (c) $10\,\Omega$ (d) $20\,\Omega$

16. A battery connected to a resistance supplies a current of 5 A. If an equal resistance is connected in parallel with the first resistance, the current supplied by the battery will be

   (a) 15 A   (b) 10 A

   (c) 5 A   (d) 2.5 A

17. The equivalent resistance of three equal resistances connected in series is $27\,\Omega$. Their equivalent resistance when connected in parallel is

   (a) $54\,\Omega$ (b) $270\,\Omega$

   (c) $3\,\Omega$ (d) $9\,\Omega$

18. An electric coil rotates in a magnetic field

   (a) in a motor but not in a dynamo

   (b) in a dynamo but not in a motor

   (c) in a motor as well as in a dynamo

   (d) neither in a motor nor in a dynamo

19. The direction of the force exerted by a magnetic field on a current-carrying wire is given by

   (a) Ohm's law

   (b) Fleming's left-hand rule

   (c) Maxwell's right-hand thumb rule

   (d) Fleming's right-hand rule

20. In a household appliance connected to the mains,

   (a) the current enters and leaves through the live wire

   (b) the current enters through the live wire and leaves through the earth wire

   (c) the current enters through the earth wire and leaves through the live wire

   (d) the current enters through the live wire and leaves through the neutral wire

II. *Mark the statements True (T) or False (F).*

1. A magnet made of a hard magnetic material retains its magnetism for long time.

2. In domestic wiring, the wires used for 15-A circuits are thicker than the wires used for 5-A circuits.

3. A heavy current drawn by a household device causes the circuit breaker to trip. After some time, the circuit breaker resets itself, restoring the current in the circuit.

4. An AC generator will work if you pass an alternating current through it.

5. The electronvolt is a unit of energy.

6. The magnetic field outside a current-carrying solenoid is parallel to the axis of the solenoid.

7. The poles of an electromagnet get switched if the direction of the current is reversed.

8. The resistance of a wire is directly proportional to its area of cross section.

9. The heat produced in a current-carrying wire is proportional to the square of the current.

10. One unit of electrical energy means 1000 watt hours of electrical energy.

III. *Below each item in the first column write the numbers of the appropriate items from the other two columns to match. (R_{eq} = equivalent resistance of the combination, i_{each} = current through each resistor, V_{each} = potential difference across each resistor, and so on)*

Column I	Column II	Column III
A. A potential difference V is applied across a parallel combination of 4 equal resistors R.	i. $R_{eq} = 4R$	1. $i_{circuit} = 4V/R$
	ii. $R_{eq} = R$	2. $i_{circuit} = V/2R$
B. A current i passes through a combination of 2 equal resistors R connected in series.	iii. $R_{eq} = R/4$	3. $i_{circuit} = 2V/R$
	iv. $R_{eq} = 2R$	4. $V_{R_{eq}} = 2iR$
C. A potential difference $2V$ is applied across a parallel combination of 2 equal resistors of resistance $2R$.	v. $R_{eq} = 1/2R$	5. $V_{each} = V$
	vi. $R_{eq} = 1/4R$	6. $V_{each} = iR$
D. A potential difference $2V$ is applied across a series combination of 2 equal resistors of resistance $2R$.	vii. $R_{eq} = R/2$	7. $i_{each} = V/R$

Very-Short-Answer Questions

1. When one volt is applied across an element, a current of one ampere flows through the element. What is the resistance of the element?

2. The figure below shows a magnetic compass placed just below a wire. If the compass is placed just above the wire and a current is passed as before, towards which direction will the needle get deflected?

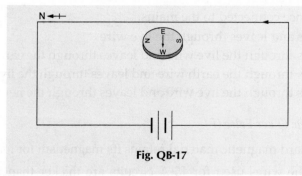

Fig. QB-17

3. If you were to connect a fuse to an electrical device to protect it, how would you connect it to the device—in series or in parallel?

Short-Answer Questions

1. Why are some materials electrical conductors while others are insulators? Explain on the basis of the behaviour of their electrons.

2. Write as many uses of a magnet as you can.

3. Why does a magnet that is free to rotate in a horizontal plane come to rest along the north–south direction?

4. There is a magnetic compass in a spaceship that has travelled away from the earth and all celestial bodies. There are no magnetic materials near the compass in the spaceship. What direction will the needle settle in?

5. In the figure below, draw a small arrow to show the direction in which a magnetic compass needle placed at the point P will point. Neglect the earth's magnetic field at P in comparison to that of the bar magnet.

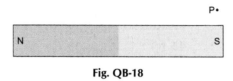

Fig. QB-18

6. Two resistances R_1 and R_2 are connected together. The resistance R_2 can be varied from a very small value to a very large value. The equivalent resistance R varies with R_2 as shown in the figure. In which way are the resistances joined—in series or in parallel?

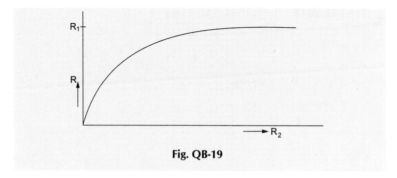

Fig. QB-19

7. Consider the two circuits shown in the figure. The cells, the material of the wires and the lengths of the wires are the same in the two cases. The only difference in the two circuits is the thickness of the wires. In which of the two will the ammeter give a larger reading?

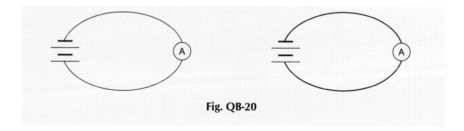

Fig. QB-20

Long-Answer Questions

1. What do you understand by a magnetic field? Does it have a direction? If yes, how will you find the direction of magnetic field at a point?

2. In houses how are devices such as fans and lights connected—in series or in parallel? Explain the advantages of the method of connection.

Numerical Problems

1. A wire of length 10 cm and area of cross section 1 mm^2 has a resistance of 5 Ω. Find the resistivity of the material of the wire.

2. What values of resistances can you get by combining two resistances of values 8 Ω and 12 Ω?

3. What values of resistances can you get by combining three 6-Ω resistances?

· ANSWERS ·

Objective Questions

I.   **1.** (a)   **2.** (b)   **3.** (d)   **4.** (d)   **5.** (a)   **6.** (a)

      7. (b)   **8.** (c)   **9.** (d)   **10.** (d)   **11.** (b)   **12.** (a)

      13. (d)   **14.** (c)   **15.** (c)   **16.** (b)   **17.** (c)   **18.** (c)

      19. (b)   **20.** (d)

II.   **1.** T   **2.** T   **3.** F   **4.** F   **5.** T   **6.** F

      7. T   **8.** F   **9.** T   **10.** T

III.   **A.** iii, 1, 5, 7   **B.** iv, 4, 6   **C.** ii, 3, 7   **D.** i, 2, 5

Numerical Problems

   1. $5 \times 10^{-5}\ \Omega\,m$ **2.** $4.8\,\Omega, 20\,\Omega$ **3.** $18\,\Omega, 9\,\Omega, 4\,\Omega, 2\,\Omega$

❖